MW00638524

CORRIGENDUM

Photos appearing on pages 62, 73, 74, 75, 76, 77 & 78 demonstrating hand feeding have been reversed. The corresponding text is correct. Feeding instruments should always be placed into the birds mouth on the birds left and angled down to the birds right.

Captions on photos on pages 122 & 132 are reversed.

PARROTS
Hand Feeding and Nursery Management

PARROTS
Hand Feeding and Nursery Management

Howard Voren and Rick Jordan

First published 1992 by Silvio Mattacchione & Co.

SILVIO MATTACCHIONE & CO.,
1793 Rosebank Rd. N.,
Pickering, Ontario, Canada L1V 1P5
Telephone (416) 831-1373
Fax (416) 831-3734

Text and Photographs copyright
© 1992 Silvio Mattacchione & Co.,
Howard Voren & Rick Jordan

All rights reserved. No part of this publication may be reproduced or transmitted in any form or by any means, electronic
or mechanical including photocopying, recording or any information storage or retrieval system, without the prior permission
in writing from the publishers.

Canadian Cataloguing in Publication Data
Voren, Howard
  Parrots

ISBN 1-895270-10-3

I. Parrots.   I. Jordan, Rick, 1958-   .   II. Title.

SF473.P3V67   1992   636.6'865   C92-093142-1

Distribution for the United States and Canada
Firefly Books Ltd.
250 Sparks Avenue
Willowdale, Ontario
M2H 2S4
Telephone (416) 499-8412

Typeset by Video Text Inc., Barrie, Ontario, Canada
Printed and Bound in Canada by
D.W. Friesen & Sons Ltd.

Contents

Parrots: Hand Feeding and Nursery Management

About the Authors

Howard Voren

Howard Voren has been involved in aviculture professionally for over 20 years. He is considered, by many, a world authority on the genus Amazona and Ara and is definitely one of the pioneers of modern psittaculture and hand rearing techniques.

Howard domestically produces and hand raises over 60 different species and subspecies of psittacines (22 different species and subspecies of Amazons) yearly.

Over the past fifteen years he has travelled extensively throughout Mexico, Belize, Honduras, Salvador, Nicaragua, Panama, Colombia, Peru, Brazil, Guyana, Surinam, Paraguay, Bolivia and Argentina; studying Psittacines in their countries of origin and collecting breeding stock for what is now, one of the most productive breeding facilities in the world.

Rick Jordan

Rick Jordan's main concern continues to be the sharing of extremely valuable hard earned information for the benefit of all aviculturists.

Whether small or large operations everyone will benefit from Rick's detailed, thorough, easy reading approach to this often intimidating subject. If as aviculturists we are to succeed in many of our stated goals of *breeding for conservation* and *assisting in relieving the pressure on wild caught individuals then we must become extremely proficient in both hand rearing and nursery management.*

Acknowledgements

Our thanks are due to all of the following, without whose assistance this book would not have been possible.

Margie Becker
Robert J. Berry
Elizabeth Danison
Judy Duke
Omar and Fran Gonzalez
Mark Hagen
Kathleen Szabo Harring
Ira Hertz
Bob and Liz Johnson
Faye Jones
Silvio Mattacchione
Mark Morrone
Tom Peterson
Karen Piesley
Pat Rose
Suni Russell
Carol Schnure
John and Julie Severts
Jean and Paul Thorpe
Jeffrey Toppel
Minnie Voren
Alfred Whitlock

Special thanks are due to Dr. Harris, Dr. Backos, and Dr. Styles for reviewing the medical information in this book.

Thanks to Julie Severts for her follow-up work in monitoring babies throughout the weaning stages.

The time involved with the preparation of this book took both of us away from our families and loved ones. We would like to express our gratitude to Kathy, Elisha, and Stacie Voren and Robert Pavese for their exceptional understanding and tolerance.

Foreword

Incubation and hand-rearing are now an undeniable and essential part of breeding parrots in captivity. Gone is the old philosophy that holds when this parrot dies we'll catch another to replace it. Indeed, the shift in philosophy has been so complete that parrot breeders now routinely consider restocking the wild with captive reared birds. This, of course, requires that great numbers of baby birds are produced regularly in our aviaries. Fortunately, modern techniques of hand-rearing and nursery management have developed along with the change in philosophy.

These modern techniques, though, have not sprung to life full fledged and ready to use. They have been laboriously and painfully pulled together over the past forty years by the experiments of a few aviculturists doing their own work in isolation. Gradually these few pioneers grew in numbers so that now hand-rearing is the norm for the majority of parrot breeders. But in the early days there were no guidelines, no books, no veterinary research, no scientifically formulated diets and, in some cases, no sympathy from fellow fanciers.

In the case of hand-rearing baby birds I was, alas, an unwilling but inevitable pioneer dragged into the struggle by circumstances. Forty years ago I was feeding canned dog food to baby birds with the eraser end of a pencil. I learned everything the hardest of ways with meager and sporadic guidance. Even so, I made a little progress based mostly on folklore, rumor, hearsay and old wives tales. As recently as seven years ago, though, I still made some very unfortunate mistakes that cost the lives of some truly rare psittacines. If the information in this book had been available to me at the time, many such tragedies could have been avoided. Fewer birds would have been lost.

Howard Voren and Rick Jordan, in the pioneer tradition, continue to explore the far reaches of hand-rearing and nursery management. By reading their book I can assure you they know what they are talking about. They write with an authority born of experience. It is greatly to their credit that they have organized, clarified and published the results of their vast experience feeding baby parrots. This is not the first hand-feeding book nor will it be the last but it is positively the best, most up to date volume now available. Indeed, I consider it the benchmark work by which all other volumes on the same subject will be measured. It is a genuine asset to the body of avicultural literature and will prove very useful to all aviculturists who want to contribute to the propagation and conservation of the world's parrots. I am very pleased to be able to recommend it wholeheartedly.

Sheldon Dingle
Past Editor
AFA Watchbird Magazine
Los Angeles, California

Introduction

As the importation of wild caught birds draws to its inevitable end, aviculturists, pet shops and would be pet owners must rely on domestic production. This ever growing demand can only be met by increasing productivity on a per pair basis, beyond what mother nature had intended. With minor exceptions, breeding pairs of psittacines in their natural habitat raise between zero and four offspring a year. The quantity of eggs laid and nestlings fledged is not only a function of protection against predators and the acquisition of sufficient food, but also the size of the bird in question. Typically the larger psittacines (macaws, cockatoos, amazons, etc.) are the least productive.

Modern aviculturists have discovered two methods to circumvent these natural limits to production. One is the *pulling* of eggs from the nest for artificial incubation. The second is the *pulling* of nestlings at a very young age for handfeeding. By interrupting the reproductive cycle the pair will usually be stimulated to nest again and produce more young than would otherwise be

Super Clutch. Part of a clutch of seventeen babies hatched in one season by pulling eggs from a single pair of Yellow Crown Amazons. Babies pictured start at one day of age and range approximately three days apart from each other.

possible. In many cases these methods have been successful and production has increased dramatically. Whether the choice is to incubate eggs or to pull nestlings at a young age the aviculturist will be left with the responsibility of feeding and maintaining nestlings that are as completely dependent as human infants.

Increased production is not the only advantage of hand-rearing nestlings. The imprinting or bonding between bird and human that is achieved when a bird is handfed, greatly enhances its pet quality. In fact, when the pet owner is fortunate enough to be the one who takes over the hand-rearing process and brings the bird through the weaning stage, the bond between the pet and owner is a rewarding lifelong experience.

Chapter 1
Managing the Nursery

1.1 General Information

When parrots are kept for the purpose of breeding and propagation the nursery and its management become an integral part of the operation. Competent hand-rearing skills can have tremendous influence on the number of chicks that will survive to adulthood. Often, parent rearing is preferred, as it is less time consuming, but this limits the number of offspring that can be reared in each breeding season. It is also interesting to note that more disease and nutritional problems are noticed in chicks that are parent-reared than in those that are reared by a proficient aviculturist.

The actual management of the nursery will vary depending on the number of chicks that will need to be hand-reared at one time. A nursery containing two hundred chicks cannot be managed in the same way as one that accommodates only two or three. The potential for disease and other health problems increases as the number of chicks increases. As the nursery caters to an ever increasing number of youngsters a greater urgency to fine tune hand-feeding methodology will arise.

To a certain degree, the management techniques employed will depend on the species that are to be reared. Hand-rearing lories and lorikeets will require a different setup than the one for rearing macaws and amazons. Additionally the setup will be different for chicks reared from day one as opposed to those that have been parent-reared for a few weeks. In situations where the nursery contains chicks that are incubator hatched and those that were parent-reared, the required management intensifies in an effort to control the potential for transmissible health problems between the two groups of chicks. Before a nursery is designed and assembled, the keeper should consider the needs of the chicks that will be reared therein.

1.2 The Ultimate Set-Up

When someone speaks of the ultimate nursery setup, it is usually from the veterinary standpoint and not necessarily the best avicultural way to do things. The ideal vet setup would be a totally sealed entity that would not allow the entrance of pathogens of any sort, such a facility would be very costly to build, equip and manage and would, therefore, from an avicultural viewpoint not be practical or functional.

To demonstrate the difficulties inherent in this type of building, consider the following rules that would have to be applied.

1. The building would have to be sealed completely air tight with some type of filtration system for incoming and outgoing air.

2. All walls, floors, ceilings, fixtures, equipment, and incoming supplies would have to be disinfected. One would ask, can food be totally disinfected?

3. Any person, before entering the nursery, would be required to shower and change their clothing. Face masks and rubber gloves would have to be worn at all times and changed often. A complete nursery outfit would have to be kept inside for each employee. This clothing could not leave the facility and would have to be laundered inside the nursery. Shoes would be replaced by disposable hospital booties.

4. Eggs to be hatched would have to be fumigated outside of the facility and hatched inside. Chicks that pipped their shells or hatched under the parent birds could not be reared inside the nursery.

5. Any chick that developed a bacterial infection or some other ailment would have to leave the facility and be reared elsewhere.

6. Employees could not be exposed to other birds during the course of the day.

Violations to such stringent rules would invariably occur on a daily basis thus making the facility impractical. One of the biggest questions asked when discussing this type of ultimate setup is whether weaned chicks leaving such a sterile environment could thrive on the outside. In theory, even the weak could survive if raised in a sterile environment. Because the immune systems of these birds would be previously unchallenged, problems might arise when taken out of their sterile environment and subjected to normal conditions.

1.3 Designing a Functional Nursery

A functional nursery would be one that works for the individual who is to staff it. If a small number of chicks were to be reared, this could be done in a corner of the kitchen or bedroom of a house. When large numbers of chicks with different origins are to be reared, a separate building may be needed to serve as a nursery. Once again, the ideal setup would be one that is designed around the number and history or origin of the chicks to be reared.

Chicks that are incubator hatched will require feeding on a frequent schedule. Accommodations for these chicks should be made in a location that is convenient for the feeder. All supplies that would be needed for hand-feeding should be kept in the nursery. This will eliminate the need to go searching for things that are necessary to carry out the nursery duties.

When designing a nursery it is best to keep in mind that the well-being of the chicks is of the utmost importance. The nursery should not be located where the chicks would be overheated, cold, or in danger of injury. Remember that children and household pets can wreak havoc on a nursery. The parrot chicks must be protected from the curiosity that is so natural to children. If the nursery is planned with the well-being of the chicks in mind, as well as the convenience of the keeper, it cannot help but be a truly functional facility.

1.4 Equipping the Nursery

Preparing a list of all that one would need in the nursery, over the course of one breeding season, might possibly fill up this entire book. The equipment that will be needed will depend on the age of the chicks to be reared. There is no need to buy a commercially manufactured brooder if all the chicks will be reared for the first two weeks by the parents. However, if day-old babies are expected, the need for a professional-type brooder or a way of keeping the chicks at the proper temperature will outweigh many other necessary items. When brooding is to take place, be sure there are sufficient electrical outlets and a back-up power source for continued service.

Medical supplies, hand-feeding equipment, and cleaning supplies will make up the bulk of items that need to be purchased. Stock plenty of syringes or feeding instruments. Food bowls and cages will need to be acquired if the babies are to be weaned in the nursery. Medical supplies can be stocked as per the suggestions of a good supervising veterinarian or aviculturist. If a veterinarian is to be involved, then antibiotics, anti-fungals, syringes with needles, topical ointments, and even surgical equipment will be very handy if they are used properly and according to professional recommendations. Medications are not recommended for those that do not have the experience to use them properly.

Paper supplies, towels, and all clean-up items are imperative. Dirty nurseries are problem nurseries. The chicks and the entire nursery must be kept clean at all times. This can become very labor intensive if a large number of chicks are to be reared; allowing the surroundings to become filthy will result in a catastrophe.

Brooding containers, bedding material, heat lamps or other sources of heat, will be among the first things used. If the nursery is set-up and stocked with these items before the chicks arrive, it will provide a smooth transition from the nest to the nursery.

The use of a refrigerator, freezer, microwave oven, clean water, and blender or food processor will make the preparation of formula more convenient. Be sure to have air-tight containers to seal formula that is to be stored in the refrigerator from one feeding to the next. In large breeding situations, some of the most functional nurseries consist of an entire kitchen area, brooding rooms, and isolation or hospital ward. However this type of setup is necessary only in a commercial breeding facility.

1.5 The Importance of Sanitation

The importance of cleanliness when dealing with baby parrots should be stressed. Young chicks are very vulnerable to disease and can be protected only through cleanliness. If sufficient sanitary measures are not taken, the chicks may be left susceptible to many diseases. Bedding that is soiled with droppings is a perfect medium for bacterial and fungal growth. It is not necessary for the chicks to ingest this fouled bedding in order for them to become ill. If the bedding contains a high bacterial growth, the chicks can become contaminated by playing with the substrate or the bacteria may enter the body through the vent.

Some fungi can be fatal if they become established in the respiratory tract of young chicks. These fungi thrive in dark, moist environments similar to damp, dirty substrate material. Once the fungi matures it will release spores into the air that are inhaled by the baby parrots. If conditions are right, the fungi will grow in the lungs and air sacs of the chick and will eventually cause death.

Even the air in the nursery is a matter to be considered. The larger the number of chicks that are being housed in the room, the greater the risk of airborne infection of some sort. The amount of feather down and dust in the air can become excessive if many chicks are feathering. Babies that have been raised under these conditions are more susceptible to respiratory infections and cloudy air sac conditions. The long term effects on health and life span of the chicks from feather down inhalation are not known. However, a disease called *feather lung*, suffered by aviculturists, has been linked to years of work in dusty bird rooms. The air in the nursery is probably the most difficult thing to keep clean. There are commercially produced air filtration systems that can clean the air and even remove some viral particles. Be cautious when using any air filter as they can dry out the air thereby causing low humidity problems. Air-conditioners and air filtration systems will require daily cleaning of the filters to keep the air at its purest.

All in all, the cleaner the environment around the chicks, the healthier they will be during the hand-rearing process. The incidence of pathogenic disease will parallel the cleanliness standards in most nurseries.

1.6 Disease Outbreak in the Nursery

Regardless of the level of professionalism followed there is always the possibility that disease can enter the nursery. The early recognition of the existence of a problem is essential in order to keep it from becoming widespread. Although a veterinarian is necessary in order to diagnose a problem and prescribe a treatment, you are the one who must be able to realize when you need this help. The following is a list of symptoms that usually accompany an illness. Whenever any of these symptoms appear in a baby bird, it should be isolated. Disease management procedures should be followed until you get an all clear from your veterinarian.

1. Any steady mortality rate no matter how small is almost always a sign of a major problem. This should be taken very

seriously especially if the mortality is among chicks of different parentage. Contrary to popular belief, sudden death in chicks that show all outward signs of good health and development is extremely rare. Unless of course they are physically killed by a feeding or handling accident. Mortality rates higher than one or two percent should never be accepted as normal.

2. Any major change in feeding response that does not reverse itself in 24 hours should be taken as a warning signal. Before illness is suspected all environmental factors should be checked. Changes in temperature, lighting and activity around the brooder can all cause temporary changes in a chick's feeding response. Formula that is too cool can drastically change a chick's feeding response to the negative. This is especially true as the chick gets older. If after checking all of these factors you find that everything is as it always was, then impending illness should be considered a likely cause.

3. Any change in the appearance of skin color from what is considered a *normal* healthy looking pink should be viewed as a serious problem. Chicks that appear to redden are usually suffering from a bacterial infection. The red appearance is due to the dehydration that will accompany these problems. Chicks that grow pale are usually suffering from either digestive failure or a viral infection.

4. Whenever chicks have a wet or slimy mouth that is not related to being fed (example: condition remains slimy one hour after feeding) they are almost always affected by a fungal or yeast infection. This condition is usually, though not always, accompanied by a whitish film or white spots on the tongue or elsewhere in the mouth. The reverse is also true. Many times the white spots or film will appear independently of a wet or slimy mouth. The spots are the actual fungal growth that is taking place in the mouth.

5. Whenever chicks begin to regurgitate a substantial quantity of formula between feedings, they are usually suffering from either a fungal or bacterial infection. The exceptions to this would be the following. Overfeeding the chick whose crop has begun to shrink because it is going into the weaning stage. Feeding food that is too cold or too sour. Feeding food that contains bitter medication. Feeding a chick that has a blockage somewhere in the digestive tract. This symptom can also be caused by certain rare viruses.

6. Whenever the passage of food out of the crop slows markedly, there is usually a problem. The problem could be a brooder that is either too hot or too cool. Both of these extremes can cause a drastic slow-down in food passage. It is also possible that the formula spoiled during storage and was sour when fed. This can also cause a drastic slow-down in food passage. Formula that has not been mixed thoroughly can continue to absorb the water in the formula and thicken (while in the crop) to the point that it causes slow passage. Most slow passage problems however, are due to bacteria and will result in mortality if left unattended.

7. When a chick appears dehydrated or thin there may or may not be a disease problem. Whether a chick is dehydrated is a judgement that is made when a chick has a *boney* appearance on the back and wings. This of course is only possible to visualize on a naked chick. Unless the dehydration or this appearance is accompanied by other symptoms it is more likely related to poor husbandry practices, than to disease.

8. When a chick shows signs of respiratory problems the cause can be difficult to determine. A *runny nose* can be caused by infection or by a sensitivity to the type of bedding used. *Gaping* or straining for breath is usually but not always caused by the inhalation of formula in non-lethal quantities. Your vet should determine whether treatment is necessary.

9. Any major change in attitude or actions from established behavioral patterns should be taken as a warning signal. Check all environmental factors. If that checks out then illness should be suspected. If there is not reversal in a few hours you should seek diagnostic help.

1.7 Pre-Breeding Season Clean-Up

As the breeding season approaches, there is much work to be done in preparation for the young. Chicks from the current year should be afforded clean surroundings so they too have the greatest advantage possible.

Plan ahead and try to estimate the number of chicks you are expecting. Be sure to stock the nursery with adequate *baby stuff* that you will be needing. Test all brooders for temperature accuracy and establish a plan in case of electrical failure.

Nurseries that have been used in previous seasons should be disinfected to eliminate any pathogens. All equipment should be cleaned and disinfected for the new season and syringes or feeding utensils should be replaced whenever possible.

Wooden items such as cutting boards, knife handles, etc. are very difficult to disinfect. Anything that can be discarded or replaced, should be. This includes any wooden perches removed from the previous year's weaning cages.

1.8 Use of Pesticides, Chemicals, and Disinfectants

Although it is important to eradicate any insects that invade the nursery, this must be done with great caution. You must always protect the chicks. The best situation is one where all of the chicks can be moved to another location and the entire room fumigated. Since this is not always possible, the use of pesticides must remain at a minimum and only those products that are non-toxic when airborne should be used. Even the discs that are stuck to a wall or counter can be dangerous to a loose bird that finds it interesting. There are a few products on the market that contain *pyrethrins* as the killing agent. If used properly, these products will pose no threat to the chicks in the nursery. Try to find products that are not pressurized spray propellants. Spray type insecticides can travel through the air and into the delicate respiratory systems of the chicks. Many times these products will be available in a paint-on type solution that can be safely used on the floor in the nursery. Limit the treated area to the perimeter of the room directly along the walls. If any odor is present, open windows or use fans and air-conditioners to ventilate the room until the odor subsides.

From time to time other chemicals may have to be used to clean the nursery. The use of products that have a strong odor is unacceptable. Strong ammonia or formaldehyde products should be avoided if chicks are present in the nursery. If there is a serious health problem that needs to be treated with this type of cleaning agent, move unaffected chicks into another room while disinfecting and ventilating the area as best as possible. At no time should bottles containing toxins be left sitting around for the chicks to investigate since there is always the possibility that they will spill and become a hazard. For this reason they should be stored in another location that is not accessible to the babies.

Disinfectants are a necessity in the nursery. They are used for cleaning the brooding equipment, counter tops, floors, and virtually all hand-rearing equipment. There are many types available on today's market and they are all limited as to what effectiveness they have to certain organisms. For this reason, suggesting only one product would be impossible. Each and every product that is available comes with literature that will tell what organisms it is effective against. They will not list the ones that they are not effective against so it is important to know which organisms must be purged in order to maintain a clean nursery. The veterinarian's office or good veterinary literature are usually the best places to find the proper recommendation for disinfectants.

Chlorhexidine solutions are the least toxic and probably the most often used in the nursery. These products are not effective against many avian pathogens. As long as the nursery remains void of the problems that cannot be destroyed by chlorhexidine, its use is highly recommended as it is one of the safest on the market. Keep in mind the limitations of these products.

Chlorine or bleach is a common and available disinfectant. Bleach is effective against most bacteria or viruses that may be present in the nursery. The biggest problem associated with its use is that, just like chlorhexidine, it loses its potency when diluted with high concentrations of organic material. For this reason anything that is to be disinfected should first be washed and scrubbed thoroughly to remove dirt and other organic matter. The chlorine must contact and in some cases remain in contact with the pathogenic organism in order to kill it.

Quaternary ammonium products are readily available from a veterinary supply source. They are used primarily to disinfect against bacteria and chlamidia but they also have limited effectiveness against avian viruses. As with chlorine and chlorhexidine, they are rendered useless when saturated with organic material and should be used on pre-cleaned surfaces only. They are safe enough to be used on food bowls and food preparation surfaces if used in a manner consistent with their labeling. Any surface disinfected should be rinsed and dried completely before it is used to serve food to the bird.

The last type of disinfectants to be recommended are called the Phenols. They are the most effective against the pathogens that affect psittacines and are not rendered useless when in contact with organic material. Phenols are highly recommended as cleaning agents for floors and cages as well as to disinfect shoes that will be worn in the nursery. The only reason they are not recommended as the only disinfectant in the nursery is that they are costly and are corrosive to most plastics and feeding instruments. The toxic effects of direct contact with birds on a long term basis is not known and therefore these products should only be used as cleaners and disinfectants.

1.9 Identification of Chicks

In large nurseries, during the height of breeding season, it can be difficult to remember which chicks came from which pair of breeders. Of course, once they have reached the age that they can be banded, keeping them organized becomes much easier. Until that time, keeping track of several chicks of the same size and species can be a nightmare.

Identification of the chicks is not only important for genetic diversity but it is, also, a valuable tool that can be used to assess the rearing successes of the breeding pairs. Knowing which chicks are the offspring of which parents can alert the keeper to certain patterns such as high mortality, stunting, repetitive illness, strange coloration traits, or recurring nutritional deficiencies. If the offspring of a certain pair of breeders exhibit any of these anomalies continuously, there may be a need to change mates or to seek a veterinary evaluation.

Chicks can be color coded for proper identification.

There are several methods of identification that can be used in order to keep track of the chicks regardless of how many are being reared. One of the most common methods is to use non-toxic, water soluble colored marking pens to "color code" the chicks. Color coding can also be accomplished by painting a small dab of fingernail enamel on the beaks of the chicks. Be sure to re-apply these colors as they wear off or fade.

Numbering systems for chicks can get quite complicated if the quantity to be monitored is large. We have established a valuable numbering system that will help to keep track, not only of the different chicks, but also the sequence in which they were hatched from a certain pair of breeders. For example, the code "YN" stands for Yellow-naped Amazon and "SC" stands for Scarlet Macaw. To these codes are added the number that corresponds to the pair that laid the egg and the number that indicates which egg it was for that particular season. In other words, "YN26" would indicate that the chick is from the sixth egg laid by pair number two. The sequence "WC53" would indicate a White-capped Pionus from the third egg laid by pair number five. When a two letter code is used to indicate the species, the third digit will be the pair number and the number or numbers after that will indicate the egg number. If more than ten pairs of a certain species are maintained, and more than ten eggs are laid from a pair, a lettering system can be initiated after pair number nine. In this manner, the second egg from pair number ten of Scarlet Macaws would be coded "SCA2" and "YNBB" would indicate the eleventh egg from pair eleven of the Yellow-naped Amazons. In very large breeding operations where more than thirty-five pairs of the same species are kept, placing an "X" before the two digit species code allows the numbering system to start all over again. Eggs should be coded on the aircell end and the number should follow the chick through the hand-rearing process until it can be banded. After banding, the old code can be annotated on the baby record for future reference.

Keeping the codes with the chicks when they are very young can be done by writing it on a piece of tape and adhering it to the brooding container. Self-adhesive address labels can also be used. Both methods will be effective when using berry baskets or plastic brooding dishes. Once the chick is large enough to be placed in brooding containers with *clutch mates*, the color coding system can be used. Be sure to annotate the baby records with the color and the letter code of each chick. The original pieces of tape can be color-coded and stuck on the outside of the larger brooder until time permits the information be put into the baby records.

Color-coding the naked chicks is done by marking the top of the head and the rump with the color of pen that corresponds to its identification. If non-toxic markers are used, there should be no permanent mark and as a matter of fact, these marks will need to be darkened frequently as they are rubbed off. We have never had an adverse reaction to the water soluble marking pens. Try to use the same color-code for chicks from the same parentage. If they are a few days apart in age and development, there will be little confusion in identifying them.

Other methods of identification that have been used include the use of color-coded plastic leg bands. These are easily removable which is one of the problems associated with their use. If they fall off or are taken off by the chick, they can be swallowed and become a major problem. When these bands fit too tightly they can cause developmental problems in the legs of some chicks. When choosing a coding system, safety is of the utmost importance.

1.10 Banding of the Chicks

Every year banding and identifying chicks becomes more and more important. In the past, banding was considered an unnecessary nuisance that served no purpose other than to possibly *hang the bird* somewhere if it were to slide the band over a loose piece of wire in its cage. Today, banding of captive bred birds is done with the use of what is known as closed bands. These bands are complete metal rings with no open seam and are available in many sizes to fit the many species that are now being reared in captivity. The proper size will be one that fits around the ankle of the bird once it has grown to its adult size. It must be put around the chick's leg at a young age to allow the bird to grow into it. The bands that are used are too small to fit over the foot of an adult of the same species. In this manner it is possible to prove that the chick was reared from a young age before the feet had grown to full size.

Open bands are those that have a slit or break in them. They are squeezed by the use of a special pliers and placed around the legs of chicks or adult birds. Because this type of band can be used on adult birds as well, it cannot be used to prove that the bird was reared in captivity. The major purpose of open bands is for the temporary identification of a specific bird. Closed-banded chicks will be of greater value than those that are open-banded because of new legislation, worldwide, requiring closed-banding in order to verify the origin of the bird. Most bands have some type of letter coding engraved in them to help breeders and other officials trace the blood lines of particular birds if necessary.

The age at which a chick must be banded will vary depending on how fast they develop. Smaller species develop at a much faster rate than large birds and will therefore require banding at an earlier age. Choose the appropriate band size for the species being reared from the list provided herein. The band must be slipped over the foot to the ankle. This is done by taking the front two toes of the leg to be banded and placing them tightly between your thumb and first two fingers. Pull the long rear toe forward with the two front ones so that the three are bunched closely together. Make sure that your fingers are far enough back on the toes so the tips of the toes are exposed. WIth the other hand, slip the ring over the tip of the three toes. Pull the band over the three toes, past the foot to the ankle. At that point the small back toe may have to be pulled through the band under the ring. With the band on the ankle and the toes in their natural position, try to pull the band off of the birds ankle. If the band

Until chicks are large enough to band, identification can be very difficult as chicks look similar.

slips off easily it is either too large or the chick has been banded too early and has not attained the desirable size for banding. If the band is of the appropriate size for the species, try banding the chick again in a couple of days.

It is very important to band chicks with the correct sized band. Remember that band sizes are based on the approximate measurements of the ankle of an adult bird of each particular species. Some people band chicks with smaller bands in order to be able to band them younger and to sell them immediately. If the band becomes too tight, it will have to be cut off, thus defeating the purpose for banding in the first place. Banding chicks with bands that are too big and loose definitely invites disaster, and is therefore not recommended. Furthermore, when domestic babies that have loose bands on their legs are purchased, it can call into question their legitimacy. Unscrupulous bird dealers have been known to lubricate oversized closed bands and painfully force them over the toes of imported birds so as to make it appear that these birds are domestic raised. Loose bands can lead one to suspect that a bird may have been smuggled and passed off as a domestic chick. For this reason it is highly recommended that the proper size bands be used so that there is never any doubt as to whether a bird is domestically produced.

If, for some reason, a band needs to be removed from the leg of a chick, it must be done carefully so that the bird's ankle will not be broken. The only safe way to remove a band is with the help of an assistant. One person must restrain the chick while the other does the work. Grab the band on one side with a pair of pliers. If the band is a closed band, it must be cut with a pair of bolt cutters or some similar tool capable of cutting through the metal. Be sure to hold the band firmly with the pliers or it may twist during cutting and could possibly break the bird's leg. After the first cut is finished it may be necessary to make another cut on the exact opposite side of the band. This will cause the two pieces of metal to separate and fall off. If the band is an open band and already has one cut in it, all that is necessary is to make another cut on the side of the band opposite the first.

Band Sizes

The following list of band sizes is from our own experience and that of friends who have shared them with us. They should be considered as *approximate* sizes for an average bird of the species listed. Exceptional cases will occur and cannot be predicted. Whenever a bird grows into a band and it becomes too snug, it should be removed immediately to prevent injury to the chick's leg. All measurments are the *inside* diameter of the bands.

Size	Species
5/8"	Hyacinth, Buffons, and large Green-winged Macaws
9/16"	Scarlet and Blue and Gold Macaws
1/2"	Red Fronted and Military Macaws, large Yellow-naped Amazons, Blue-crowned Amazons, Mealy Amazons, Yellow-crowned Amazons, large Double yellow-headed Amazons, Moluccan Cockatoos, Umbrella Cockatoos, Greater Sulphur-crested Cockatoos.
7/16"	Red-lored, Lilac-crowned, Orange-winged, Red-headed, Blue-fronted Amazons, African Grey Parrots, Citron-crested Cockatoos, Medium Sulphur-crested Cockatoos and some Lesser-Sulphur-crested Cockatoos and Goffins Cockatoos.
3/8"	Larger Mini-macaws, Yellow-shouldered Amazons, Yellow-faced Amazons, Citron-crested Cockatoos, Lesser Sulphur-crested Cockatoos and Goffin's Cockatoos.
5/16"	All Pionus, Small Mini-macaws, Hawk-headed Parrots, White-fronted Amazons, Yellow-lored Amazons, Large Conures, Moustached Parakeets, Ring-necked Parakeets, Alexandrine Parakeets, Caiques.
9/32"	Gold-capped, Jenday, and Sun Conures
17/64"	Orange-fronted, Peach-fronted, and Brown-throated Conures
1/4"	Smaller Conures, Monk Parakeets, Brotogeris, Meyer's and Senegal Parrots, Plum-headed and Blossom-headed Parakeets
3/16"	Cockatiels and Lovebirds

1.11 Record Keeping

Records are kept on chicks to document their lineage, weight progress, health, and history. Accurate record keeping is important to the future of aviculture as this provides a detailed account of the chick's progress through the various stages of its life. Even small operations will benefit by keeping a record about each and every chick that is reared.

Keeping track of the developmental progress of a chick can be very helpful to the novice or veteran hand-feeder. Formulas can be assessed for their effectiveness on the different species or weights can be compared to those of chicks that have been previously reared. Needless to say the more detailed your documentation the greater will be your probability of success with all future babies. For more information on record keeping see section 6.2 of this book.

Chapter 2
Maintenance of Nestlings (Brooding)

2.1 Temperature

The temperature at which a chick is brooded can be as important to its survival as proper feeding. Keeping very young chicks too cool can spell certain death. Most developmental or *failure to thrive* problems that occur in the first ten days of life are related to brooding temperatures that are too low. The effect of brooding can be demonstrated if two identical two-week-old birds are brooded at temperatures ten degrees apart. This will result in a major difference in their growth patterns. There is a need for research to be performed on the effects of brooder temperatures on chicks of all ages.

When examining records from many of our previous breeding seasons, a few interesting facts were revealed. The first observation was that chicks that were reared early in the year, during the cool weather of the breeding season, were healthier and *better doers* than those hatched and raised in the hot time of the season. This was also true of the chicks that have been raised in Central America over the years. This observation has since been confirmed by several other professional aviculturists and additional comments included that the clutches were larger, and the babies appeared to be healthier in the early spring as opposed to those reared in the heat of the summer. The second interesting fact that was uncovered and confirmed by others is that the first chick hatched thrived better than those hatched later. This may be due to the fact that the first hatched is brooded warmer as the hen continues to incubate the remaining eggs in the clutch.

After considering the observations above, a regime of brooding in the same manner was established. Newly hatched chicks are kept at hatching temperature (98.5°F) for approximately two to six hours after hatching. Early or weak hatches may benefit from additional time at this temperature. After this initial drying period, the chicks are placed in a brooder set at 97.5°F for about four or five days. This brooding methodology is an attempt to give each chick the *first chick* advantage that seems to occur naturally. The results have been very positive and this regime is now recommended as standard procedure.

After about four or five days, the brooder is reduced to 95°F for the next five to nine days. Smaller species that develop at a much quicker rate than the larger ones will be moved to the lower temperature brooder at an earlier age. At about ten days of age, chicks are kept at about 93°F until they have sufficient down feathers for them not to be considered naked babies. In smaller species this may be only a few days, in larger birds, such as macaws, it could be a couple of weeks. Once the down feathers are reasonably developed the chicks can be kept at 85°F. When the feathers cover the wings, head and the breast is partially feathered, the chicks can be kept at room temperature (78-82°F). From this point on, temperature adjustments are made only by observation of the chicks comfort. Panting chicks are too warm and huddling lethargic chicks are too cold. Once partially feathered, the chicks should be comfortable at room temperature.

The number of chicks that are brooded together will have a major influence on brooding temperatures. Chicks that are brooded separately will require a little more heat than those that

Young chicks must be kept very warm as their down offers poor insulation. Pictured is the bright yellow downed Yellow-faced Amazon.

are brooded together. It is critical that chicks brooded alone be kept at the proper temperatures as they have no other babies to huddle with if they become uncomfortable. Once the chicks have feathered, brooding temperatures are not critical as long as they stay within the 78-82°F range. Remember, babies that are fully feathered are easily stressed by being overheated. In larger commercial operations the chicks experience less health problems when they are maintained in air-conditioned rooms below 85°F.

With the exception of the first five days of life, the above temperatures are not critical. These ranges have worked well on a continual basis so little experimentation was carried out on other temperatures. It is important to brood incubator-hatched chicks at temperatures just barely below that of incubation. This will reduce the stress until the chick is capable of producing some body heat of its own.

Incubator-hatched chicks have different temperature requirements than chicks that have been brooded by the parents. Babies that are pulled from the parental nest at ten to twenty days of age will usually be acclimatized to a much lower temperature range. These babies are not kept at a constant temperature at all times. When the hen leaves the nest to rummage for food, the babies begin to cool and must rely on each other for heat. This cooling can cause a slowing of digestion, and even development, but this is of no consequence to chicks that are a week or older. The hens return to the nest, feed the chicks and begin brooding again. These temperature interruptions are what helps a chick to acclimatize to variable warmth. Chicks that are taken from the nest after having been acclimatized in this manner seem to be able to digest food and develop normally at cooler temperatures than incubator-hatched young.

When adjusting brooding temperatures for the chicks, be sure to consider their former environment. Nest-hatched chicks that are raised in the hot summer months will tolerate higher heat better than those hatched in the cooler weather. The history and comfort level of the chick will be the final determining factor as to the best temperature to maintain them.

When a thermometer is not available or is just not feasible, there are a few observations that can be made to help determine if the temperature is correct. If only one chick is being brooded, place the very tip of the wing between your lips. If the chick is warm enough the wing tips should feel sufficiently warm. If they are cool or cold to the touch, the brooder temperature should be elevated. This method is to be used on chicks that have not yet feathered as it is difficult to assess the actual temperature of the bird through the feathers.

As the babies get older and begin to grow down feathers, their behavior can be very important when assessing their comfort level. Chicks that sit with their feathers fluffed are using their insulation capabilities to keep warm. This is an indication that the chick is too cool. If more that one chick is being brooded in the same container, the way they *clump* together can be used to determine the proper temperature. The tighter they bunch together, the colder they are. This activity is true of smaller, naked chicks also. If the smaller, more susceptible, chick is left on the outside, this could result in a problem. As the temperature is increased towards the correct setting the chicks will bunch together in a looser manner. When they are completely comfortable they will lie next to each other with minimal body contact. The opposite is also true. If the chicks spread out in the brooder so as to not be in physical contact with their nestmates, they may be too warm. If the heat increases to the extreme, they will often pant and feel very warm to the touch. In these cases the temperature should be reduced immediately. When young and of the brooding age, comfortable chicks usually spend most of their time sleeping, not running around, panting, or flapping their wings.

2.2 Humidity

Although humidity is a critical factor in successful incubation it is much less important in the rearing of chicks. Most parrots that are being reared in captivity do well at a relative humidity of 40% or above. If maintained at the low end of this range, humidity can cause some flaking of the skin and possibly even late feather growth. If the humidity remains very low for extended periods of time, and the formula contains inadequate water to sustain the chick, dehydration may occur and cause all of its associated problems. There should not be any major slowing of growth or development unless the humidity drops below the 40% relative mark.

Chicks that are brooded in high humidity environments may feather a little early but this will not be noticeable unless the humidity is maintained, for substantial amounts of time, on the high end of the scale. Continued wetness will cause premature feather growth at the expense of body size. When high humidity is accompanied by moisture, it can promote the rapid growth of fungi which could cause health problems in the chicks.

Changing the humidity in the chicks environment can be accomplished by humidifying the entire room. Commercial or home-sized humidifiers are available that are capable of increasing the humidity in the entire room. If the brooding humidity of only one or two brooders needs to be elevated, placing small bowls or jars of water in the brooder should do the trick. Be sure to put these water containers where there will be no danger of a chick falling inside or spilling them.

When it is not feasible to humidify an entire room and the brooders used are not enclosed to hold humidity, a small area of any room can be converted into a high humidity zone. This can be accomplished by masking off an area with sheets of plastic, being sure that there is ventilation above and below. In this area place a fish aquarium half full of water with a submersible aquarium heater in it. Adjust the temperature of the heater to provide the adequate humidity to the area. The actual level of humidity can be measured with a hair hygrometer or wet bulb thermometer.

2.3 Lighting

In general, the overall lighting of the nursery is more important for the convenience of the hand-feeder than it is for the chicks. Lighting does have some effect on growth which is explained in section 7.2 of this book.

Fluorescent fixtures give excellent overall lighting of the nursery. Chicks should be kept in semi-darkness during rest periods as this is easier on their eyes. No matter what type of light is used, it should provide the keeper with adequate lighting to observe the chicks and to complete all of the hand-rearing chores safely.

If light bulbs are being used as a heat source for brooding, it is suggested that they be colored bulbs. Amber or red bulbs are most often used as they soften the light that the chicks must tolerate twenty-four hours a day. Light bulbs have been used at our aviaries for the past fifteen years. In the beginning, we were concerned that white light bulbs may have a detrimental effect on the chicks' sight later on in life. Some of the chicks that were reared under these bright lights still reside at the aviary and none of them are experiencing any trouble with their eyes. However, out of empathy for the chicks, amber colored bulbs are now being used. The chicks sleep better and are more content under subdued lighting.

If light bulbs are not being used as a heat source, a night light is suggested in the nursery room. As a chick grows older, it seems to become more insecure about being in total darkness. When the lights are suddenly turned on in a previously pitch black room, many of the older birds will go into a screaming panic. The following true story will illustrate my point:

> I was called in to consult on a problem that an overseas exporter had with a large group of amazons being housed indoors. Every night the entire group would go into a panic and scream several times. First a few would start to scream in fear and within seconds the entire group of three hundred birds would scream and batter themselves against the sides of the cage. The exporter tried everything, including bathing the birds in "Holy Water", to exorcise the spirits. All of his efforts were to no avail. My suggestion was to place two night lights (small 15 watt bulbs) at either end of the large room. This action stopped the midnight panics caused by these "Demons".

2.4 Space

The space that is necessary to brood nestlings depends on how many need to be accommodated at a certain temperature. Chicks should be able to stretch out and lie down without touching each other. If the area or bucket is too large, the chicks may move around frequently which could cause a developmental rate change (see chapter 7.2).

As the young birds grow and begin to feather they need enough space to stretch their wings and legs. At times they may even flap their wings as if they are trying to fly. This type of exercise is important to the development of wing coordination and also helps to develop the musculature of the breast and back. The space required to brood two or three macaws together need only be enough for one to stretch at a time. There is no need for a huge container to accommodate all three flapping birds at once. The other option would be to place them into separate buckets in order to allow them to exercise. Remember that there are certain advantages to small brooding buckets and limited space. This is especially true of the very young chicks that are still in a rapid growth stage. If older chicks constantly climb out of buckets they should be removed from the brooder and transferred to small cages.

2.5 Bedding (Substrate)

Young chicks that are to be kept in the nursery must have some type of bedding or substrate in their brooding containers. Many breeders use some brand of facial tissue or paper towels for chicks that are very tiny. Paper towels can be too abrasive and have been known to cause bleeding of the delicate feet or wing tips. Some of the newer, extremely soft, facial tissue that are non-abrasive are often too slippery and have been known to cause blistering in chicks. These slippery tissues may add to the splayed leg problems that are encountered in some babies due to the feet slipping on the bedding.

When brooding newly hatched chicks, it is not recommended that wood shavings be used as the initial substrate. It is extremely important to monitor the droppings from very young chicks and the use of wood shavings makes this virtually impossible. After about a week on the tissue, chicks can be brooded on some other soft bedding material or wood shavings. Do not place chicks of this age on wire.

The most commonly used substrate is pine shavings. Wood shavings are used because of their absorption capabilities. They come in many different grades and grind textures. The best type to use are those that are shaved very thin and very small with a minimum wood dust content. Shavings that are polluted with too much dust may cause respiratory or eye irritations. Chopped wood products can be dangerous if they contain hard chunks of wood that could be swallowed and cause crop impacting. If ingested, even large shavings can impact a crop.

With the increased interest in breeding and rearing parrots in captivity has come a wide choice of manufactured beddings designed specifically for birds. Some of these products are made of ground corn cobs, pelleted grass fibers, or recycled paper products. The corn cob bedding and the pelleted grass fibers are supposed to be digestible if swallowed by the chicks. The digestibility depends on just how much bedding they swallow. The biggest problem with these two products is that they do not provide a very good foot-hold for the chicks and, if layered deeply in an attempt to correct this, the chicks sink into the substrate. The recycled paper products offer good absorbency, traction, and even limited digestibility but are somewhat costly to use in large quantities.

Diapers and paper towels are commonly used by aviculturists as a substrate for older chicks. We find it difficult to recommend these as the chicks usually end up lying around in their own fecal matter. This is also true of cloth towels or wash cloths. Some materials may contain loops of loose thread that will catch the chicks toenails and cause injury. When used, these substrates need to be changed frequently to keep the chicks clean.

Some bedding material can be toxic. The use of cedar shavings can cause respiratory problems in chicks that have a sensitivity to it. This sensitivity appears to be more prevalent in amazons, especially those of the *ochrocephala* group. There may be others that will develop this problem as well. Many aviculturists have used cedar for years, without experiencing any problems, yet others seem to encounter this complication almost immediately. In severe cases, the chick may actually die from the respiratory inflamation that results from the use of cedar.

Many of the commercial landscape mulches have been used as bedding but most of these are too dirty and full of bacteria and other contaminants. Young chicks will often chew the bedding material that is used. For this reason it is never suggested that potentially dangerous or dirty substrate be used.

The latest trend in the search for the perfect bedding material is the use of food items. This is an attempt to eliminate the deaths and other problems associated with the ingestion of the substrate. Rabbit pellets, fine dog kibble, and pelleted bird diets have all been tried. Their absorbency capabilities are limited and they become tainted with bacteria and fungi once they are soiled with wet fecal matter. Whatever substrate is used, the necessity to keep it clean is of the utmost importance. This applies to the nesting material in the nest boxes as well. Dirty babies will quickly become sick babies.

2.6 Types of Brooders

The types of brooding buckets or containers that can be used to brood chicks is limited only by your imagination. Everything from paper bags to expensive plexiglass, climate controlled, units are successfully used as brooders. What you use will depend on the age, size, and number of chicks to be raised as well as their temperature requirements.

Some of the most commonly used brooding units and containers are listed below. The comments that follow each section are not pointed at any particular product but are experiences that the authors wanted to share.

Human Baby Incubators and Intensive Care Units:

These units are very accurate and reliable. They will usually maintain the correct temperature even if the room temperature fluctuates a few degrees. Most of these units come equipped with a water reservoir to allow humidity manipulation. The air filtration system cleans the outside air before it is pumped to the heating unit and eventually into the brooding compartment.

In some cases, depending on the model and cabinet you purchase, cleaning and disinfection of this type of unit is somewhat labor intensive. In some models, it is not feasible to keep birds that have feathered, as the feather down clogs the air systems and renders them useless. Although somewhat costly, if chicks are to be hand-reared from a very young age, these brooders can be highly recommended for their accuracy and functionality.

Fish Aquariums:

Aquariums constructed of glass or plexiglass are commonly used to brood young chicks. In a pet store they can be very advantageous as they take up very little space and allow the chicks to be viewed without handling. This also allows babies to become accustomed to human traffic around them.

If heat is desired or necessary, a heating pad can be placed under one half of the bottom and the chick placed on towels inside. The heating pad should not cover the entire bottom to allow an escape route if the pad should get too hot. On rare occasions where the chick has come in contact with the glass bottom of the tank, severe burns of the chick's abdomen have been reported. This can result in the need for surgical removal of portions of the skin and crop of the chicks.

There are a few obstacles associated with these tanks that should be considered. They are heavy and can be easily broken. Cleaning them can be a chore as they will need to be submerged in water or hosed and disinfected. Some aviculturists believe that babies raised in these tanks suffer from undue stress because they cannot hide from outside traffic. When raising chicks to be used as future breeders, the outside of the tanks can be painted black to provide greater privacy.

Human infant incubators make excellent brooders for small chicks.

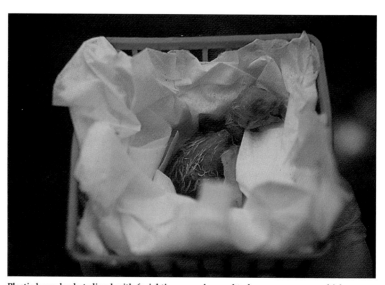

Plastic berry baskets lined with facial tissue can be used to house very young chicks.

During the first five days of life, chicks should be brooded in separate containers.

These five day old Macaw chicks have been moved to a community brooding container.

Chicks should be brooded with other chicks of the same approximate size.

Chicks should be brooded with other chicks of the same approximate size.

Commercially Produced Baby Brooders:

There are now several commercially produced baby brooders on the market. These vary in price, heat sources, humidity control, and size. To date, there are none that have an air filtration system built into each unit but some do have a method of air circulation.

Inexpensive models can be purchased to use as separate brooders for each clutch of babies. These units are usually constructed of styrofoam or plastic. Unfortunately many infections that can spread through a nursery are airborne. These types of brooders provide no protection against an airborne contaminant. It makes very little sense to spread the babies into several small, separate units if they are all going to be sitting on the same table breathing the same air.

Some of the available models are very difficult to clean and disinfect properly. Those that use light bulbs as a heat source are totally inadequate for chicks in the first week of life, as the heat can never be regulated properly. During a power outage some other method of brooding will have to be sought. Most of them look great and will give a professional appearance to the nursery, but their usage should be assessed before purchase.

Commercially produced brooders constructed of plastic or plexiglass and heated with warmed water are available. They have separate water tanks that use heated water to provide the correct environment for the chicks. A submersible aquarium heater heats the water to the approximate temperature requirement and the heat transfers through the plastic to the special compartment for the chicks. There are certain advantages and a few disadvantages to these units. One big advantage is that they are the only brooders that will remain warm for some time during a power outage. The warmed water takes several hours to cool and will provide heat to the brooding chamber during the entire cooling period. Most of them are small and inexpensive enough that they can be used to separate chicks into small groups or clutches. The disadvantages include the limited air circulation in the chamber, the potential for extremely high humidity from the heated water, and the fact that they are very heavy and hard to clean when filled with water.

Heat Sources for Brooding:

If the brooding unit chosen does not come with a heat source, this will have to be provided in order to supply the necessary heat to the chicks. Common sources of heat include light bulbs, heating pads, or even space heaters that heat the entire room. There are a few cautions associated with each of these.

When using light bulbs they are usually mounted in clip-on lamps. These lamps mount to the edge of the brooding container or a nearby shelf. Be sure the clip fits tightly and cannot come loose allowing the entire assembly and hot bulb to fall into the container with the chicks. Overheating may occur if the lamp is too close to the babies. Observe the comfort level of the chicks and adjust the distance accordingly.

Light bulbs do burn out! If they burn out when no one is looking, the chicks will get cold. Larger babies will probably be able to survive until the next feeding time when someone notices the bulb, but very small chicks will have problems if exposed to extreme temperature fluctuations. Use colored light bulbs to provide a more tolerable environment. The colored bulbs give off the same amount of heat per watt as the white bulbs do.

Heating pads are a very common source of heat for brooding. The biggest problem is that none of them are thermostatically controlled. They work on a regulator system that keeps the unit heating for a certain amount of time rather than to a certain temperature. The higher the setting, the more time the regulator allows the pad to heat. This can be a potentially dangerous situation and has been known to actually *cook* babies. Many parrot chicks can recover from extreme cold, but not from extreme overheating. Many times the overheated chicks appear to have recovered only to die later from organ damages that occurred.

Another consideration when using heating pads is an escape route if the pad gets too hot. Always leave some space in the brooding container where the pad does not contact. If the chick gets too hot, it may move over into the cooler zone. Unfortunately, the younger chicks usually do not do this and may require constant supervision. With older chicks the heating pad can be hung on the inside wall of the brooding container rather than under the substrate. This allows the chick to move away from the excess heat if necessary. Unfortunately, young chicks that have not yet opened their eyes are not always this clever and will often wander off into the cool sections of the container or sit in the overheated areas.

Brooders controlled with light bulbs are prone to over and under heating problems. Since they heat from above, the severity of overheating is usually minimal. Chicks that are overheated from below can sustain injury easier than those heated from above. This is because the organs of the lower abdomen are directly against the skin in the belly area but are insulated by muscle and bone from above.

If the nursery room is heated to the brooding temperature, there is no need for supplemental heat. In sufficiently warm rooms, it will not matter what type of brooding container is used. The problem with this is the inability to provide less heat to the older chick or more heat to the younger. One solution to this problem is to keep the room about 80-85°F and brood young chicks together in a container with a heat source. As they grow, separate them into their own containers to avoid overheating.

Paper Bags:

Using brown paper bags as brooding containers is inexpensive and very convenient. They completely eliminate the need for cleaning and disinfection of brooding containers as well as changing of the substrate. When they are soiled, they can be discarded and a new bag with a small layer of substrate is used. Since they do not come with a heat source, this will have to be provided. Snobbish aviculturists may think they are not fancy enough but they are very sanitary, require little maintenance, provide a more natural environment, and are disposable. When raising babies for future breeding they are highly recommended as they simulate the same type of feeling that a baby would get in the nesting box.

Cardboard Boxes:

When chicks become too large for paper bags, they can be transferred to cardboard boxes. The box provides all of the advantages of the bag plus a little added support. Reflector lamps can be clipped to the side to provide any needed heat for the chicks. As the babies get older, wire bottoms can be fitted inside and they can be used to start the weaning process. Boxes need to be changed often when they become soiled with feces or food.

Plastic Tubs, Bins, and Bowls:

Plastic containers that are suitable for holding baby birds come in a great variety of shapes, colors, sizes, and even prices. Almost every variety that has been manufactured has been used to hold chicks, even the throw away margarine dishes from the grocery store and plastic flower pots. There are several benefits in using these containers. One, they are easily cleaned and disinfected. It is also possible to lay a piece of wire material inside of these containers to prevent the chicks from consuming the substrate. The only caution that should be mentioned is that there seems to be a correlation between some crooked beaks and the rounded inside surface of some bowls. If macaws or other larger birds are being brooded in plastic containers, it may be wise to choose a square or rectangular shaped one.

As with the boxes or paper bags, these containers are only to house the chicks. There still remains the need for some type of heat source. When chicks are very small, plastic bowls used in conjunction with a commercial brooding unit provide an efficient brooding system.

2.7 Brooding: The First Five Days

During the first five days of life there is a strong need to monitor each chick separately from its clutch mates. Small plastic containers such as berry baskets or margarine dishes from the supermarket work very well as holding containers. These allow

Plastic bowls are often used as brooding containers for a clutch of chicks.

for individual monitoring of feces and make it easy to separate chicks in the same brooder. Line these containers with facial tissue to be used as substrate. Since temperature is critical at this stage of development, the chicks will need to be housed in a unit that can be temperature controlled. These units are discussed under section 2.6, Types of Brooders. Extreme temperature fluctuations during these first stages of life can be harmful or fatal to the chicks.

2.7.1 Brooding: From Five Days to Pinfeathers

As the chicks grow a little older, they will be less affected by temperature variations and incorrect brooding techniques. With these new tolerances come some flexibility as to how the chicks will need to be brooded. At this age, if development is progressing normally, chicks will benefit by being placed in brooding containers with *clutch mates* or other birds. All baby birds are more content when housed with other babies. It is not necessary to move chicks from the brooder where they are presently housed as long as temperature adjustments can be made and there is adequate space for the chicks to move.

2.7.2 Brooding: Heavy Pinfeathers to Partially Feathered

At this stage in development, heat requirements diminish considerably. If the nursery room is warmed to a comfortable level, there will no longer be a need for supplemental heat. Chicks of this age begin to slim out for future flight capability and are prone to eating the substrate material. This is the reason that many choose to place these almost grown birds on wire. They are not as comfortable as they would be on soft bedding material but the risk of ingestion takes priority.

There are many advantages to keeping chicks on wire. They will have limited access to their droppings and the wire will prevent them from playing with the contaminated bedding material. Place some type of absorbent material below the wire to help keep the container clean. Bottoms of cardboard boxes can be removed and the wire bottom stapled in its place. This makes for very easy replacement of the paper or substrate below by lifting the box, bird and all, and placing it on a clean foundation. When chicks begin to climb out of boxes or containers that are of a sufficient height, it is time to move them to a cage.

Heavily pinfeathered chicks being transferred to a cooler brooding environment.

Well-feathered chicks require less heat for brooding.

2.7.3 Brooding: Well Feathered to Full Feathered

The final step is to cage the birds. Most commercially produced bird cages have wire bottoms that are spaced too far apart for young chicks. It may be helpful to cut a piece of 1/2" x 1/2" wire to cover the cage bottom. This will provide a better platform for the chick to sit on. At no time should a chick be placed in a cage that has no bottom. This will allow it to play with droppings and spoiled food items.

If supplemental heat is required, clip on lamps are most convenient when using cages to house the birds. Place them down low so the chick can huddle near if extra heat is needed. Healthy, full feathered chicks, should be comfortable in a wide range of temperatures. Occasionally one will fluff its feathers and should be provided with the additional heat until it adjusts to its new environment.

Chapter 3
Formulas

3.1 Recipes and General Nutritional Information

There are probably as many recipes for hand-feeding formulas as there are aviculturists. Each of us adds our own special ingredients to try and enhance growth or digestibility. If you are raising your own bird from a very young age you must make your own decisions as to what works best. If you have purchased your bird from a pet shop, always follow the advice of those who sold you the bird. Generally, they have the experience and knowledge to know how the bird should be fed.

The most commonly used recipes are monkey biscuit based formulas. There are also a growing number of prepared formulas marketed specifically for hand feeding psittacines. These are supposed to be nutritionally complete. Unfortunately, at the time of this writing, most of these were nutritionally inferior for feeding to birds from a very young age. Many people who use these formulas stir in one or more of the additives commonly found in ingredients of monkey chow or biscuit formulas. Hopefully someone will create the perfect prepared formula to be used on all types of parrots. When that day comes we will be among the first to praise its existence. Even though most of them do poorly when used on a long term basis, some are sufficient if used for the last few weeks of hand-feeding, just prior to weaning. At this point in time a bird's growth pattern is all but completed and nutritional requirements are not as stringent as in the time of rapid growth. Whatever the base formula consists of, some of the most commonly used additives are listed below. Many of them have some advantage if used in the proper proportions but caution must be used not to dilute the basic formula to the point that it no longer works.

- Vegetable oil
- Peanut butter
- Sunflower meal or seed (hulled)

- Wheat grass powder
- Mixed vegetables (human baby food)
- Powdered non-fat milk
- Powdered whole goats milk
- Strained carrots (human baby food)
- Liquid vitamin supplement
- Yogurt
- Acidophillus supplement
- Apple sauce
- Oatmeal
- Ground millet
- Papaya or other fresh fruits

All of these additives have beneficial value but should be used only in limited quantities. If too many additives are used, or quantities used are excessive you can create a nutritional imbalance in the formula. The additives chosen will depend mainly on the type of monkey biscuits that are used. When using the oily type monkey biscuits, there is no need to add vegetable oil to the formula. Vegetable oil, sunflower oil, peanut butter, or sunflower seeds are used to raise the fat content of the formula. Although cockatiels and cockatoos do well on a low fat formula, most South American species (macaws, amazons, conures, etc.) do not.

Wheat grass powder and mixed vegetables are used in order to supply chlorophyll and beta carotene as well as other trace nutrients that are considered by many to be nutritionally important. Powdered milks have been used to enhance the overall nutritional value of formulas. In fact, many healthy chicks in Central and South America have been raised on nothing but raw milk and corn meal or wheat bread. Recently the use of milk has fallen out of favor with many aviculturists. This is probably due to the results of a few experiments conducted in California that show some psittacines may have a sensitivity to lactose. The inclusion of milk products in the diet can cause loose droppings if the bird has any intolerance to lactose. As stated previously, many birds benefit tremendously from the inclusion of milk (raw, whole milk or powdered milk) supplements to an otherwise deficient formula. The benefits far outweighed the occurrence of loose or watery droppings. Consider the fact that even human babies have loose droppings when fed on a milk diet.

Strained carrots and vitamin supplements have been used to enhance the vitamin content of certain formulas. If the formula has been cooked prior to use, vitamins can be added after the formula has cooled in order to replace the ones that are destroyed by heat during the cooking process.

Yogurt or acidophillus supplements are used to supply the bird with beneficial bacteria that aid in digestion and help to protect against bacterial infection in the gut. These products must be added after the formula has cooled to serving temperature because excess heat will destroy the live cultures. If yogurt is used and is to be of any benefit, it must contain live cultures. Many manufacturers kill these cultures to extend the shelf life of the product. The benefit of the addition of yogurt products is still questionable. At the time of this writing there are a few psittacine specific bacillus products available on the market. If a lacto product is needed, it may be best to try one that is made specifically for parrots, not for other animals.

Apple sauce has been used by many in order to speed up the passage of food out of the crop and through the digestive tract. This is added to prepared formulas more often than to monkey biscuit based diets. It should not be necessary if the diet is formulated correctly and is of proper consistency.

Many aviculturists use a different recipe for the first week of life. That is, different from the one used through the weaning stage. We have experienced very positive results when using a 50/50 mixture of *Pedialyte* or *Ricelyte* and *Ensure Plus* in the first week after hatch. The *Pedialyte* or *Ricelyte* are excellent for immediate hydration if fed as the first meal. This is fed alone or with an acidophillus supplement if available. *Ensure Plus* (vanilla) is a liquid nutrition product made for adults with nutritional absorption problems. The *Ensure Plus* is mixed 50/50 with the *Ricelyte* for the first five days. After this time, regular formula, thinned to the proper consistency, is used. Do not mix the Ensure mixture with the regular formula. For best results, the change over is done on an empty crop.

Many aviculturists use a very watery mixture of their regular formula during the first few days. If the basic formula is deficient in needed nutrients, by adding water, the thinned formula becomes even more deficient. It may supply the much needed hydration that all chicks require but the proteins and fats will not be present in sufficient quantities.

Formula #1 (Voren's Aviaries) Approximately 13% Fat

This formula is excellent for South American species. When feeding cockatoos or any bird that does better on lower fat diets, eliminate the sunflower oil and add only 1/4 cup of hulled sunflower seed. Spiralina powder can be used in place of the wheat grass powder. Either product produces excellent results.

Ingredients Needed:

50 Zoo Preen Primate Chow Biscuits (5% fat)
1 Tablespoon Wheat Grass Powder
1 Tablespoon Sunflower Oil
1/2 Cup Hulled Sunflower Seed
5 Cups Water (Distilled)
Avian vitamin supplement

Place all ingredients into blender and liquify until smooth. Pour mixture into microwave safe bowl and cover with 1/8 inch of water. Cook in microwave on high until boiling, making sure the center is hot also. Remove from oven and add ice cubes or water to bring to proper temperature and consistency. Serve immediately. Just prior to serving, a good avian vitamin supplement can be added in minimal quantity.

Formula #2 All Common Psittacines

This formula is only a slight variation from the many that are commonly used. It is a good all around formula to be used on most psittacines that are raised in captivity today. It has been fed to most birds from Cockatiels to Hyacinth Macaws with good results.

Ingredients Needed:

50 Zoo Preen Primate Chow Biscuits
2-4oz. jars of creamed corn (Baby Food)
1-4oz. jar of garden vegetables (Baby Food)
1 heaping tablespoon of peanut butter (no salt)
small amount of *Nutrition Plus* Vitamins

Soak primate chow in water until soft. Add enough water to cover biscuits and stir together. Microwave until boiling along the edges and stir again. If additional water is needed, add in small quantities. Once heated thoroughly, remove from oven and add all ingredients except for the vitamin powder. Can be cooled and thinned using ice cubes or water until it reaches serving temperature and consistency. Using a blender to liquify this formula is advantageous. Just prior to serving, sprinkle lightly with vitamin supplement. When freezing this preparation for use at a later time, do not add vitamins until serving time. Freezes well in ice cube trays and stored in air tight plastic bags or containers.

3.2 Consistency

The thickness or consistency of normal formula is very difficult to describe. Many people describe it in many different ways and by naming various products. For the first week, formula is fed thin as described in the section *Getting Started with Day Old Chicks.* After the first week, food is fed at what would be considered *normal consistency.* The only way to describe this thickness would be to name a few commonly known foods such as oatmeal, cream of wheat, thin apple sauce, cake batter, or yogurt. If the formula resembles one of these in consistency, it is probably acceptable. The best way to mix food is from experience. If there is an experienced person that can be contacted, this may be the solution to the problem. Never feed food that is so thick it remains in the crop for hours longer than it is supposed to. On the other hand, after the chick is a week old, never make the food so thin that it digests in one hour. Experimenting with the type and thickness of your own formula will yield a mixture that will be correct. The consistency will also be slightly different depending on the type of feeding instrument to be used.

3.3 Sterilization

Formulas made with monkey chow or any animal biscuit should be boiled or at least, heated thoroughly. The fact that your formula will be a saturated solution means that the moment you are finished blending it, it begins to grow bacteria. It is therefore best to start out with a formula that is as clean as possible whether you are going to feed it or store it. The formula should be cooked after it is blended together. This is because the aeration process that takes place during blending contaminates the formula with whatever happens to be floating around in the room at the time. The best method of all is to store the formula uncooked and prepare in the microwave just prior to feeding. The best way to accomplish this is to blend the food rather thick and cool it with ice cubes after boiling. The ice cubes bring the formula down to serving temperature and the water that melts from the cubes thins the formula to its proper consistency. At this point, just prior to feeding you should add a vitamin supplement, in minimal quantities, in order to make up for vitamin destruction caused by the heat. This is also the time to add any acidophillus supplements you wish to use. Culturing your formula with beneficial bacteria is recommended if the product used is a psittacine specific acidophillus product. Unless the bacteria supplement is derived from birds it will not take hold in the digestive tract. Remember that just because the container states, *for use in birds*, does not mean that it is derived from birds, and specifically, parrots.

Prepared formulas are usually manufactured in a way that gives you a clean product. If they have been stored properly between manufacture and consumption they should not have to be boiled. Most of them are, in fact, precooked prior to packaging. Some of them, if cooked a second time, become nutritionally deficient.

Quality control is of extreme importance. Feeding clean formula not only helps keep the bird from contracting a bacterial infection, but also slows down the fermentation process in the formula. It is this fermentation process that causes the formula to turn sour and is the major cause of the ailment called sour crop.

3.4 Taste

The taste of most monkey chow formulas is readily accepted by most young chicks. If bitter or strong medication must be added to the formula, many chicks may shy away. Sometimes the bitter-taste can be disguised by the addition of sugar to the formula. If the medicine is extremely unpleasant, the reaction of the chick can be anything from reluctance to feed to regurgitation of the food. If you prefer not to sweeten the formula you may have to cope with the problem for only a day or two. Most babies will get used to the offensive taste of some medication if you are persistent. If they do regurgitate they will usually leave a little in their crops. Until they are accustomed to the taste and hold an entire crop full without regurgitation, you will have to feed more frequently. Never under dose the recommended medication amounts in order to make them hold it down. Under dosing of medications can be dangerous. If the problem persists consult your veterinarian.

Most prepared formulas have a pleasant enough taste to be accepted by the chicks. Some, however, do have a strong flavor which can be distasteful to a bird if they have been fed another type of formula previously and you switch them suddenly. If the chick must be switched to a new formula and it does not accept it immediately, try mixing small amounts of the first formula into the second to provide them with a familiar taste. Slowly decrease the amount of formula that is mixed in and the bird will wean off of one and on to the other.

The thing to remember is that birds usually react negatively to any strong taste whether it is bitter or sour. This is true unless they have been fed the strong flavor from an early age.

3.5 Storage

The proper storage of formula is very important to the health of the chicks that are being fed. After cooking, homemade formulas should be cooled as quickly as possible. As stated in the section on sterility, the best way to do this is with the use of ice cubes. This allows you to place the cooled formula into the refrigerator or freezer directly after cooking. The temperature drop caused by the ice cubes enables your refrigerator or freezer to quickly reduce the temperature of the formula to the proper levels to inhibit bacterial growth. By slowing or stopping harmful bacterial growth it is possible to keep the formula from becoming sour as quickly as it normally would.

If formula is to be refrigerated, it is better not to prepare more than will be used in a twenty-four hour period. If it is to be frozen, store in containers that will hold the quantity that you are going to use for one feeding. Containers that hold the exact amount that will be used can be defrosted and heated in a microwave oven before each feeding. If only a few babies are being fed, formula can be frozen in ice cube trays and only the right amount of cubes thawed and used at each feeding. This allows you to store the formula in small blocks. Once they are frozen solidly, the cubes should be removed from the tray and placed in an air tight container or sealable plastic bag for longer storage.

Excess formula that has been heated but is left over should be discarded. In fact, any prepared formula that is left standing unrefrigerated for any length of time should be discarded. Most formulas are high in nutrition and are perfect breeding grounds for bacteria. A wasted bowl of food is always preferable to a sick baby and a trip to the veterinarian.

Pre-formulated mixes should never be prepared with water until the moment you are ready to use them. Any leftovers should be discarded as with the homemade formulas. These pre-formulated powders should always be stored in airtight containers to prevent moisture from being absorbed into the mix. Once the powder becomes moistened from humidity or a wet spoon that has been used to dip in the container, bacterial or fungal growth can cause contamination. Keep all dry ingredients to be used in hand-feeding formulas in a cool place. Storing them in the refrigerator or freezer in air-tight containers is recommended but not necessary.

3.6 Blending and Mixing

When blending a homemade formula or when mixing a pre-formulated mix with water, it is important to consider that some mixtures take longer to absorb water than others. Often a mixture will appear to be of the correct consistency but will thicken after standing for a few minutes. If the formula thickens too much after it is ingested, it can lead to slow passage of food out of the crop. This caution is especially true for pre-formulated mixes because they are usually prepared by hand rather than in a blender. Determine how much the formula thickens while standing and add sufficient water during mixing or blending in order to offset the thickening. If water must be added to a homemade formula after it has been cooked, always add the water and stir by hand, do not use a blender. If you use a blender you will have to re-sterilize due to the bacteria that may enter the formula during aeration.

Although pre-formulated mixes are not supposed to be stored after mixing with water, this can be done as an experiment to determine how much it will thicken after standing in the crop for a couple of hours. The test can be performed at room temperature and the formula discarded after observation.

3.7 Heating and Re-heating Formula

Formula that has been prepared and stored, either in the refrigerator or the freezer, must be heated before it is served.

This is usually done in a microwave oven. These ovens are known to create hot spots in the food. Thoroughly stirring the mixture until the temperature is consistent throughout will alleviate any danger caused by the over heated spots. The microwave also allows you to heat the formula in the same container that will be used to hold the food when feeding. The invention of the microwave oven has been a real boon to aviculture. The inconvenience of having to pull out the cook pot, light up the stove, and wash the pot every few hours has been eliminated from an already busy schedule of timely feedings. Anyone who cannot be trusted to stir out the hot spots caused by the microwave should not be trusted to feed baby birds.

Those who wish to heat formula in a pot on the stove must remember not to use the heated pot to serve the formula. The formula should be transferred into a bowl at room temperature because the bottom of the pot, still hot from the stove, can further heat the formula after you have stirred and tested it for the proper temperature. The extra heat that may be added could raise the temperature of the formula to a dangerous level.

When feeding chicks from day one, or where small amounts are necessary at each feed, there are a few other methods of heating the food that may be more convenient. Day old chicks will eat only 1cc or less per feeding. These small quantities cannot be heated efficiently in either a microwave or a saucepan. An easy way of heating one syringe full of food is to immerse the entire syringe in water that is heated to the proper feeding temperature. The food inside will reach the desired temperature in a few minutes. More than one syringe can be heated in this manner, if needed. It is important that the temperature of the water is the same as required for the food. The warm water will insulate and keep the other syringes warm while the first chick is being fed. Small quantities of formula will cool as rapidly as they heat. If it takes too long to feed the chick it may be necessary to place the syringe into the warmed water for another minute in order to re-heat it.

If a prepared formula is to be used, heating may be a bit easier. These formulas should be prepared with water that is hot enough to make the food the correct temperature when the mixing is complete. These *just add water* formulas are meant to be mixed and served immediately, not mixed and stored for later use. Do not re-heat them in the microwave or many of the nutrients may be lost during the heating process.

3.8 Variations in Formulas for Different Species

To date there is very little *real* scientific data concerning the nutritional requirements of parrots. It is known that some formulas do a better job than others but it is usually not known why. Unfortunately, the only people that are, at present, *testing* most of the pre-formulated mixes are those who are trying to sell them. There are only a few of these companies that actually have their own experimental flocks of parrots to use for their research. Most will distribute their product for field testing and have no control over its use, so that data provided can be misleading. Look to the professionals when trying to decide which formula to use. Your pet shop or commercial breeder should always be consulted when making these decisions. It may be wise to use only the products that are manufactured by companies that maintain research flocks and do not rely on biased information from aviculturists.

From personal observation it is apparent that Macaws and Conures do not do as well as Cockatoos and Cockatiels when fed on some of the lower fat diets. We have seen many Cockatoos and Cockatiels grow beautifully on diets that range between 3% and 5% fat content. Macaws and Conures raised on these fat levels are too slim. Requirements of fat for Macaws and Conures are better maintained somewhere between 10-15%. This level of fat produced birds with full rounded breasts up through the weaning stage. Whether these fat levels are necessary for every South American bird, or whether they are needed due to some unknown deficiency in the diet is unknown at this time. Those who are raising a bird from a very young age should be concerned with these requirements. A bird that has been started and only requires a few weeks of feeding to get it through weaning will probably not suffer from a deficient fat content in the formula. The fat content of any formula can be easily raised by the addition of vegetable oil to the mixture. Again, consult the experts before making a decision.

Some species of parrots may have nutritional requirements that are presently unknown. For example, the fig parrot group does not do well on most of today's hand-feeding formulas. The exact nutritional requirements for these birds have not been established. This is also true of some of the rarer parrots that have not been in captivity very long. Monkey biscuit based formulas are more efficacious than baby food based or premixed formulas. If the species in question has never been hand-reared in captivity, it may be preferable to try a monkey biscuit formula first. To this can be added a product that contains any known deficiency that exists in this particular species. When rearing difficult species it is beneficial to have an analysis of the diet that would normally be eaten in the wild. These wild diets are usually not feasible as a hand-rearing formula but variations of existing formulas can be derived and will, in many cases, suffice.

3.9 Digestive Enzymes

Recently, digestive enzymes have been added to the ingredient list of additives for hand-feeding formulas. The major benefit from the use of these products will be noticed in chicks that exhibit a typical failure to thrive or grow. In some cases these chicks are suffering from decreased digestive efficiency from the under-production of these enzymes. If this is the reason, it will respond almost immediately to the addition of digestive enzymes. The daily weight gains and apparent growth should increase within twenty-four hours. Newly hatched chicks that fail to gain weight or lose weight may benefit from enzymes also. The two most commonly used products are *Prozyme* or *Pancreazyme* which were originally formulated for older dogs and cats that develop nutritional deficiencies. The dosages listed on the bottles are for small mammals. When adding this to the hand-feeding formula, very small dosages are needed. If adding to a full bowl of formula, use approximately one-quarter to one-half of a teaspoon. This is enough product to dose about one quart of formula. The moment the enzymes are added to the formula, they begin to break down and predigest the solids so that the formula becomes very watery. Allow the enzymes to work for a few minutes prior to feeding the formula to the chick but never store it after it has been mixed.

It has proved basically harmless to normal chicks so if only one chick needs to have enzymes added to its formula, it will not hurt to feed it to all of them. The usual usage period is about one week before the chick improves and begins to digest more efficiently. Once a noticeable improvement has occurred, discontinue the use of the enzymes. If the chick continues to do well, there will be no benefit in the continued use of the product.

In normal and healthy developing chicks there is no benefit to using digestive enzymes. Experiments have been conducted that show no weight gain nor developmental differences when these products are added to the formula of normal birds. The only interesting fact is that some stress lines in the feathering of certain birds have been blamed on the overuse of digestive enzymes. Much has been said about the use of these products to thin the formula to feeding consistency instead of using the required amount of water. The enzymes thin the formula without diluting the amount of solids contained therein. Theoretically this allows a thinner more manageable formula to be fed, which should contain more nutrients without dilution. Some people use these enzymes to reduce the number of times they have to feed in one day. They feel that the chick is getting more nutrition in less quantity. Our experiments have not demonstrated that either of these goals are attained by the use of digestive enzymes. In fact, the chicks that were fed the enzyme formulas were actually thinner than those fed normal formula. This is probably due to a poorer hydration of the tissues from the fluid deficient diet. There is little benefit from the use of these products unless a chick is having problems absorbing nutrients because of a natural lack of its own enzymes.

3.10 Temperature of the Formula

The temperature of the formula should be warm enough to elicit a feeding response but not so hot that it scalds sensitive tissue. Proper temperature plays an important role in getting the bird to respond favorably at feeding time. The feeling of warmth in the baby's mouth is one of the main cues that triggers the feeding response. This is the back and forth head jerking movement that baby birds make when being fed.

Younger birds are more sensitive to the heat but, at the same time, they will respond to a formula that is cooler whereas an older bird may not. As the baby gets older it becomes more finicky and the formula must be warm enough or they may not respond. It is better to err on the cool side but if the food is too cool, the baby will not respond. As with human baby formula the best place to test its temperature is on the wrist. Remember that the crop holds a large quantity of food in an area where the heat does not dissipate quickly. Care must be taken not to make the formula so hot that it burns the crop. In very young birds, too hot food (even though it's not hot enough to burn) can damage the crop in a way that causes it to loose its elasticity. This contributes to the condition known as pendulous or sagging crop which usually leads to motility problems and acute sour crop. For more information on feeding temperatures, see section 5.4, Temperature of the Food.

3.11 Lactobacillus

The addition of a lactobacillus product to the hand-feeding formula can never be harmful. However, many of these products are derived from the gut flora of other animals such as swine or cattle and show little benefit when used on parrots. Although these microbes have the same name as those that are found in birds, they have evolved in the digestive system of mammals and, therefore, do not have the ability to adhere to the intestinal tract of birds in order to eliminate potentially harmful bacteria from gaining a foothold. The companies that manufacture these products present them as digestive aids only. Unfortunately, many of the companies that distribute them try to sell them as something else. Remember that just because a label states *Lactobacillus for birds* does not mean that the product was derived from birds. Theoretically the addition of lactobacillus should be of extreme benefit to the chick in helping to impede the growth of harmful bacteria. There is no proof that these products promote increased weight gain or growth rates.

Several new products have recently been introduced that are derived totally from the flora of psittacines. These products are now available in many countries and it is hoped that they will populate the intestinal tract of the chick with *good* bacteria that will help it to resist invasion of harmful bacteria present in the feeding formula or environment. If the intestinal tract is populated with this good bacteria, there will be no room for the harmful or gram negative bacteria to take hold and it will be forced out of the system.

Chicks usually hatch with no bacteria at all. Within the first day or so, the chick absorbs normal gut flora from its food and from the environment to populate the digestive tract. If gram negative bacteria take hold first, the chick may eventually become very ill and will have to be treated with antibiotics.

In an effort to establish whether or not lactobacillus products have any effect on parrot chicks, we performed a few experiments of our own on a varied sampling of birds. The objective was to determine if the culturing of chicks with these *beneficial* bacterial preparations would in fact be effective in preventing harmful bacteria from gaining a foothold during the hand-feeding process. All chicks in this experiment were cultured with these bacterial preparations the moment that they hatched. In some cases the egg was opened just prior to hatching in order to assure that they were being cultured before any other bacteria had a chance to begin colonization. This was accomplished by mixing the lactobacillus with dextrose or a rice syrup based electrolyte solution and feeding it to the chick just prior to hatch. These feedings were continued for the first week of the chick's life. Six to ten weeks later, the preparations derived from other birds such as poultry, appeared to have very little effect on the bacterial makeup of the chicks intestinal tract. The psittacine specific preparation, however, showed a marginal effect on the final culture. The presence of the potentially harmful bacteria was reduced or eliminated as long as the birds were not challenged in any major way. As soon as we challenged a group of chicks by allowing the bedding to get dirtier than normal, the harmful bacteria was able to colonize the gut. In short, these chicks failed a challenge, living in the contaminated nesting areas, that would normally be no problem for parent reared chicks. Perhaps in the future a superior psittacine product will become available that will be a major breakthrough in preventative medicine. For the time being, strict sanitation of formula and brooding areas are our only way to ensure that chicks have a good strong start in life.

3.12 High Calorie Additives

When chicks are suffering from a disorder that limits the amount of food digested, high calorie additives can be added to the formula to ensure that the chick receives some nutrition. Only supplements that are low in fat will be of any benefit as a high fat content will slow the passage of nutrients out of the crop. The usual method of use is to mix the supplement with an electrolyte solution and feed it instead of formula. This is done until normal passage of food is resumed. These supplements can be a big benefit to an infirm chick but should not be used, or especially overused, with normal birds. The addition of high calorie supplements to a normal bird's formula may make it too rich and cause substantial slowing of digestion and sour crop.

3.13 Vitamin and Mineral Supplements

Individuals that prepare their formulas from scratch may benefit from the use of a good vitamin or mineral supplement. Prepared hand-feeding formulas are supposed to be nutritionally complete and the addition of vitamin supplements may be dangerous.

Formulas that are cooked prior to serving can be deficient in vitamin A content. The heating process tends to destroy this vitamin as well as some others. Any vitamin supplement must be used sparingly to avoid possible toxic effects from overdose. Water soluble vitamins such as Beta Carotene, A, B, or C, pose little risk as the excess will be washed out of the chick's system but fat soluble D3 and A can be fatal if overdosed. If the formula is known to be deficient, supplementation will do no harm. Vitamins should be added when the formula has cooled to serving temperature.

3.14 Chlorophyll

The one ingredient that is always present in parent-fed wild diets is chlorophyll. The health benefits of this nutrient are well documented in many animal diets but most hand-feeding formulas do not contain chlorophyll and would be improved by its addition.

A few years ago, spinach became a popular additive to many formulas but rumors that it might block the absorption of calcium ended its popularity. We have been using wheat grass powder for a few years and can recommend it highly as a supplemental additive to any hand-feeding formula. Wheat grass is not only high in Chlorophyll and Beta Carotene but contains a multitude of other trace nutrients as well. A noticeable difference in the overall plumage coloration was seen with the use of this product. The *reds* will be especially brilliant. Consultation with nutritionists has revealed that this is probably caused by the high beta carotene content of the powder. However, simply supplementing the beta carotene content of a formula will not produce these brilliant red feathers. The use of wheat grass powder, spirilina, or other products rich in chlorophyll is highly advocated and we believe no formula should be without it.

3.15 Experimental Additives

At the present time quite a few experimental additives are being tried by aviculturists. Most of these are coming from the shelves of health food stores and their benefits remain to be seen. Some interesting ones would be the use of garlic extract to eliminate candida problems, aloe juice to enhance overall digestion and health, yucca extract to eliminate the ammonia in the digestive tract and droppings, and echinacea to boost the immune system. Most of these additives have not been documented as to their benefits in baby parrots, nor does anyone agree on the amounts to be used in the formula. In the future, some of these will probably prove valuable. Care must be taken when using any experimental additive as certain species may have an intolerance to their use. For now, the ones mentioned above have proved harmless when used in small quantities.

Chapter 4
Feeding Instruments

4.1 General

The method of feeding and especially the tool that will be used on the chicks is a personal decision. The feeder must use what is comfortable for them rather than something that is highly suggested by others. If used improperly, any feeding instrument can become a dangerous weapon.

Different species of psittacines will be easier fed using a certain feeding instrument. Some people become so proficient at using a spoon that they can feed almost any type of bird and not have formula flying all over the walls. On the other hand there are those that just cannot manage the spoon and the activity of the chick at the same time, for these people it will be better to choose another method to feed. The feeding instrument is only a tool to be used to deliver the food into the birds mouth or crop. Some may work better when feeding Lories but not work at all when feeding a Macaw. These are the experiences that are so beneficial if shared with other aviculturists.

4.2 Bulb-syringes

Bulb syringes are one of the more commonly used tools for hand-feeding. It consists of a rubber bulb that fits into a wide syringe body. The rubber bulb acts like a plunger to pull up the formula or to push it out. They range in size from 20cc to 60cc. These are very handy for feeding large birds. It is not unusual for a macaw to take 140ccs of formula in one feeding. The 60cc syringe bulb can hold up to 140cc of formula at a time. This is accomplished by allowing the formula from each draw to pour down into the bulb after it is in the syringe. With the pointed end up and the first 60ccs down in the bulb, you can depress the bulb, turn it down into the bowl and draw up a second time. After that it's good for about another 20ccs. This allows you to completely feed a large macaw without having to put the feeding tube back into the formula after it has been in the bird's mouth. This is advantageous if feeding more than one bird from the same bowl of formula.

4.3 Piston Syringe

The piston syringe is probably the most commonly used implement for hand-feeding. They range in size from about 1/2cc to 60ccs. These syringes are usually calibrated and marked clearly to make exact measurements easy to regulate. They are available with two different types of tips. The catheter tip and the luer tip. The latter is used primarily to administer medication through a needle. The catheter tip has a wider opening on the end that makes it easier to draw and expel feeding formula. It may be easier to feed very small chicks using the luer tipped type. For larger birds the catheter tip is preferred as it makes the task much easier due to the increased amount of food that can fit through the tip.

4.4 Spoon Feeding

This instrument is probably the original tool used to hand-feed baby birds. Many breeders and bird shops still use them. It makes the job of feeding a slower but more personal experience. The sides of a normal spoon are bent up to simulate the lower mandible of the parent birds and so that the spoon will hold more formula. Normal procedure is to spoon feed the formula to the babies one spoonful at a time. Many people feel that spoon fed birds wean easier than those that are fed with a syringe. This is probably due to the personal touch that is given to spoon fed babies and the fact that they taste and swallow the formula before it enters the crop. Spoon feeding does simulate the natural feeding that would take place by the parents but it is a slower, less efficient method if numerous chicks are being fed.

If babies are initially fed using a syringe or catheter tube, they will often resist the transition to eating from a spoon. The first problem is that the bird is used to being approached with a syringe and may find the spoon to be a strange item. With patience this problem can usually be solved in very little time.

The second problem that may be encountered is the time difference between syringe feeding and spoon feeding. Birds that have been fed with a syringe may become bored and refuse to eat after only a few spoonfuls of formula. This also will pass with a little patience.

4.5 Glass or Plastic Pipette or Eyedropper

Newly hatched chicks or chicks that are very small may be easier fed using a pipette or eyedropper. The pipette resembles an elongated eye dropper with a long neck which enables the feeder to direct the formula to the exact spot they want it. These can also be used to administer oral medications. Eyedroppers may be available from the local drug store or veterinarian's office. The plastic version can be purchased in large quantities and discarded after use.

4.6 Catheter (Tube)

A catheter is a feeding tube that is meant to go directly into the crop of the bird. These tubes are placed on the end of a bulb or piston syringe. This allows the hand-feeder to fill the crop directly from the syringe. They are usually made of soft rubber as they were originally designed to be used as a urethral catheter for humans.

Injuries can occur from the incorrect use of these tubes as feeding devices. After repeated usage and soaks in the disinfectants, the rubber begins to harden and could become an injurious sword that may lacerate the internal areas of the mouth or crop. Whenever a catheter is used to feed, caution must be taken not to force it into the trachea or through the delicate membranes that line the esophagus and crop.

The biggest advantage to using a catheter is that a bird that refuses to eat can be force fed in minimal time. Many aviculturists that are feeding numerous babies at once will use the catheter as the main feeding instrument due to ease and time efficiency.

4.7 Gavage Needles

The gavage needle or tube is a metal feeding tube designed to direct formula or medicine directly into the bird's crop. They are usually constructed of stainless steel and have a small round ball on the end to prevent rupture to the crop. The same precautions should be used for the gavage as for the rubber feeding tubes. The metal tube is a very dangerous tool if used improperly. It takes very little pressure to force the end of one of these through the esophageal wall or directly through the bottom of the crop. They are available in the United States from certain specialty businesses that deal with bird supplies. When feeding debilitated birds with no feeding response, they are an invaluable tool.

Chapter 5
Feeding

5.1 General

After all of the decisions concerning brooding, formulas, and feeding instruments have been made, they must all be combined with proper feeding techniques in order to achieve success. Even the most professionally designed facility will fail if the babies are not fed and cared for properly.

5.2 Getting Started With Day Old Chicks

Feeding day old chicks can be slightly intimidating to the novice. This is an unnecessary feeling as, usually, tiny chicks have a strong will to survive and will elicit a stronger than expected feeding response. Weaker chicks normally grow stronger after only a few feedings.

Small chicks will require small feeding instruments. Glass eye droppers, small syringes, or spoons will usually do the job. It is usually best if the feeder is at eye level when feeding small chicks. This allows for close observation of the chick during feeding. Very small chicks need to be kept warm during the actual feeding process. This can be accomplished by using a swing arm lamp and a 100 watt light bulb. If chilled, many will refuse to eat or may become ill.

Hydration is far more important than proper nutrition to a day old chick. Chicks will actually do better on a nutritionally incomplete electrolyte solution than on a nutritionally complete formula. For this reason it is recommended that the first feeding consist of an electrolyte solution which contains an energy source. Several brands are available at the drug store. *Pedialyte*, or *Ricelyte*, are the two most commonly sold in the United States where they are marketed for human infants as a rehydration solution. To this you need to add some type of liquid nutritional supplement. One product that can be highly recommended is called *Ensure Plus* or *Ensure* powder (Ross laboratories).

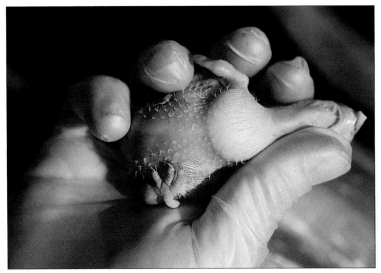

Well-rounded breast from excellent hydration during the first five days.

Normally developing healthy chick showing slim breast from poor initial hydration.

Ensure Plus comes in a liquid form and is vanilla flavored. The *Ensure* powder is probably more convenient as it has a much longer shelf life, up to two weeks, and can be mixed as needed. Once the cans of liquid have been opened, they can be stored in the refrigerator for only approximately 36 hours.

Mix the *Ensure Plus* liquid to a solution of 50/50 with the electrolyte solution. When using the *Ensure* powder, do not use the electrolyte solution to reconstitute the product. This may result in over-hydration of the chick and could cause its death. It is best to mix the powder with an equal measure of water and then prepare the 50/50 percent solution to be fed to the chick. These preparations should be fed exclusively for the first three to five days of life. Do not mix them with the hand-feeding formula.

Failure to properly hydrate a chick in the first few days can cause the chick to become a *poor doer* throughout the rest of its development. During the first day of life, babies will do better on a nutritionally incomplete electrolyte solution than they will on a nutritionally complete formula even if it is prepared very fluid. To better understand this concept it may be helpful to consider the following analogy. Think of the newly hatched chick as a partially dry sponge. If you wet (hydrate) the sponge it will expand (grow) and show an increase in weight. It will also become more supple and functional (viable). If instead, some of the water is withdrawn, the sponge will shrink in size and weight (dehydrate and become thin). It may also become hard and useless (dead). A newly hatched chick reacts much the same way. If in the first day or two the chick is fed a very thick formula with minimal water content, the digestive system will draw on what little body fluids it has stored in order to digest the thick formula. Often this will cause a dehydration problem and crop stasis from which the chick may not recover. If formulas are fed that are only marginally adequate in fluids, the chick may appear thin from under-hydration and it usually remains thin for the remainder of its time in the nursery. Anytime chicks hatch that are dehydrated, they usually will not live through such poor treatment.

These are the reasons why it is very important to hydrate chicks from the beginning. Properly hydrated chicks appear full and round in the chest and usually remain so if maintained on a proper diet.

As mentioned above, chicks are fed exclusively on the hydration formulas for three to five days. After this time, they are switched to a thinned (more fluid) version of the hand-feeding formula on which they are to be raised. The slow addition of formula to the hydration mixtures has proven to be unnecessary. It is usually considered a good practice to mix formulas together when a dietary change is made as this reduces the stress that often occurs. Our experience with using the *Ensure* products shows it is not beneficial and may actually be harmful in some cases. For some unknown reason, some babies will experience crop stasis and a resulting sour crop when the mixture of the formulas reaches a 50/50 percent dilution so it is best if the chicks are switched over suddenly from one feeding to the next. This has never proven to be a problem.

Another strange situation will occur if a chick suffers from a bacterial infection while being fed the *Ensure* hydration mixtures. The mixture will curdle in the crop. The crop contents will separate into a watery layer and a thickened sediment layer similar to soft cheese. This sediment is actually the congealing of the proteins caused by excessive bacterial buildup. Make sure the product fed was fresh before assuming that the chick has a bacterial problem in the crop or digestive tract.

If this situation arises, the bad food must be removed from the crop. This is easily accomplished by forcing the hardened

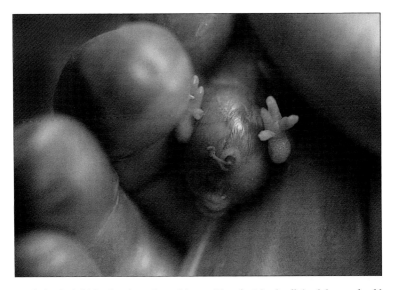

Newly hatched chicks showing substantial quantities of retained yolk in abdomen should be fed only fluids until they cease to pass fecal matter.

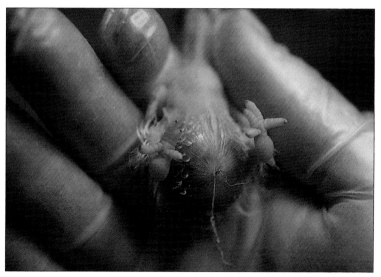

Chicks hatched with little or no visible internal yolk-sac can be fed formula immediately.

substance up the esophagus and into the mouth. From there it is removed by using some type of tool or the handle of a small spoon. Perform this procedure quickly but be cautious that there are no fluids present that may come up the esophagus and aspirate the chick. Babies that experience this problem should be switched to a thinned hand-feeding formula mixed 50/50 with an electrolyte solution.

The quantity to be fed for the first feeding will vary depending on the size of the chick. Very small chicks may take as little as .1 or .2cc where larger chicks may take up to 1 full milliliter on the first feeding. The vast majority of parrots that are raised will usually fall into the .25 to .5 milliliter category. With each feeding there is a need to stretch or dilate the crop just a little. When feeding solely liquid care must be taken not to aspirate the chick. Thinned formula is less likely to be aspirated but the risk is present when using either diet.

The first few days after hatch, the crop of the chick must be steadily increased in capacity or the chick will not attain its maximum growth potential. If the crop is not stretched at the proper rate, even if the chick is fed every time it is empty, it will still not grow as well as one that has increased crop size. When feeding the electrolyte and liquid nutritional diet it is very difficult to increase crop capacity. Although it is important to increase the crop capacity by increasing the amount fed each feeding, it must be done with extreme caution when using a totally liquid diet.

The following example of food increases are based on the use of a thinned regular formula. If using the liquid diet for the first few days, the increases will be 50% less and any increase should be accomplished with caution so as not to aspirate the chick.

When feeding a thinned formula, the first feeding on a medium to large sized bird, like an Amazon or Macaw, will usually range between .25 to .5ccs or milliliters. Observe the swallowing of the chick with each tenth of a milliliter to insure that it goes into the crop and does not back up into the lower esophageal canal. Observation should be easy due to the lack of feathers and the extremely thin skin of the chick. After each drop of formula is introduced into the mouth of the chick it will swallow and force it into the crop. When the crop reaches its capacity the food will be visible as it builds up in the crop entrance on the side of the chick's neck. When it appears that formula is about one half of the way up the neck, no more formula should be fed. When feeding chicks of the larger species you will find that they will often accommodate .5ccs on the first feeding. The crop should be taut to the touch. Be careful not to push too hard on the crop and accidentally force the formula upwards. The first feeding will be equal in volume no matter what formula you are using.

Using Macaws and Amazons as an example, it is found that most will easily take approximately one half of a milliliter on the first feeding. This will be true of either formula or fluid diet. At the starting point, increase the amount fed by a fraction of a milliliter at each feeding so that at the end of the first twenty-four hour period the crop has stretched to hold one milliliter. In the case of the liquid diet, it is often acceptable to reach about .75ccs. When using regular formula stretch the crop on a daily basis by the same volume that was fed at the end of the first twenty-four hour period. In other words, if the crop was holding one milliliter at the end of the first day, it should hold two at the end of day two and three milliliters at the end of day three. Continue these increases for about five days. After five days, stretch the crop at will. In smaller species that will only hold, for example, one quarter of a milliliter on the first feeding, the crop capacity may only be one-half of a milliliter at the end of day one. In this case, increase the crop size by the factor of one half milliliter per day for the first five days. When feeding the

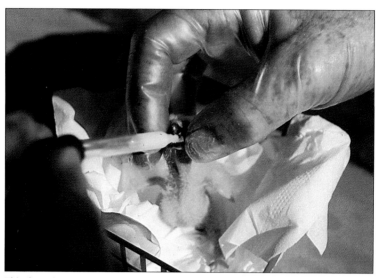

This three-day-old African Grey chick is large enough to have its beak gently pried open by insertion of eyedropper tip.

This five-day-old African Grey is now large enough to be fed with a small glass bulb syringe.

liquid diet the volume will be increased on a daily basis by a factor of 50% of the volume fed at the end of the first 24 hour period. The feeding of liquid diets and formulas create some problems that do not exist in the nestbox. Parent fed birds do not receive liquids in the quantity they would when they are hand-fed. The chances of a chick aspirating on liquid in the nest is rare compared to one being hand-fed. It is for this reason that young chicks need to be supported in the upright position for brooding and sleeping. The use of small brooding containers padded with facial tissue or some type of soft paper is recommended. Support the chick's body and chin in such a way that it will remain upright and will not lay down allowing the liquid to come up the neck and cause aspiration.

The actual feeding process for newly hatched and very tiny chicks is slightly different than that for the larger ones. Hold the chick's head upright between the thumb and forefinger. Try to use feeding instruments that have small tips to administer the formula. This will allow you to gently pry the beak open without actually having to do it with your fingers. Once the warm formula touches the beak or inside of the mouth, the chick will usually elicit a feeding response and open the beak. Sometimes it is not possible to get the tip of the feeding instrument into the beak of the chick. It is usually possible to dribble formula over the tip of the upper beak and allow it to run into the lower mandible. The best point to do this is near or on the egg tooth. In most parrot chicks, the lower mandible is larger and extends wider than the upper beak. Whenever food is dripped onto the upper beak it automatically runs into the lower mandible. This is best accomplished by lifting up the head and tilting it slightly backward. When using syringes that have a wide opening in the tip, the opening can be slipped over the tip of the upper beak. Formula will flow out around the beak tip and into the mouth. Always be careful to feed slowly when dealing with new hatches or very young chicks. Allow each drop to be swallowed before introducing the next one.

Day old chicks benefit from being fed as often as possible. Regardless of the species or size of the chick, the crop will usually hold enough food to maintain it for about two hours. The first few times the baby is fed, the formula seems to digest faster. You may find this is also true of chicks that are fed in the morning or after any period of fasting. This is because the food passes from the crop into an empty digestive tract. Babies that are fed every two hours will develop at a faster rate than those fed every three hours. The result will be the same but the chicks that receive a strong start are usually fuller and more robust throughout the entire hand-feeding process.

Weight gains are always better on chicks that are fed on a frequency schedule of every three hours. They will also be able to tolerate a rest period of six hours during the night and will still maintain approximately the same growth pattern as those that are fed every hour around the clock. Once a frequency is set, it should not be changed or the growth and development may suffer (see section 8.33 Stunting Syndrome). Over-stretching the crops of very young chicks, so that they can hold additional food for longer periods of time is almost always a certain death sentence. The young chicks cannot handle the stress of repeatedly having their crops emptied manually in order to avoid sour crop.

5.3 The Feeding Response

A bird's feeding response is the head-jerking activity and vocalization it makes while it is being fed. This response is triggered by gently applying pressure to the corners of the mouth or the fleshy pads on the upper sides of the upper beak. The exact location and the amount of pressure required for the optimum reaction varies among birds of different species and among individuals of the same species.

The importance of the feeding response is that it tells you the chick is soliciting food and is prepared to swallow food that is introduced into the mouth. Many chicks will stop responding just before they stop swallowing to take a breath. If the feeding response stops, the deliverance of formula into the mouth should stop. If the response cannot be initiated again, and you feel the chick should receive more formula, proceed with extreme caution. Place small quantities of formula into the mouth to see if the chick will continue to swallow even though the feeding response has stopped.

The beak structure of a hatchling usually reveals some information as to the location of the pressure point. Birds with large fleshy pads near the back of the beak will usually respond when touched on one or both of these pads. Those with notched beaks will respond when touched near the notched section and some may respond when touched anywhere near the beak.

To better prepare yourself for feeding a new chick, experiment by touching the chick with the tips of your thumb and forefinger. Vary the amount of pressure used at the corners of the mouth. Also experiment with touching different areas of the upper mandible to see if you get a stronger response when you touch a particular spot. If you get a strong response you will not have to worry about choking a baby unless the food is fed too quickly. Make sure that your fingers are not too cold. If this is the case you may fail to get a response. Sometimes a chick that will not respond to the touch of your fingers will respond to the feel of the edge of a warm spoon touching the inside corners of the mouth. In cases such as these the chick may be better off fed with a spoon for a while and switched to some other method at a later time. If the response is discontinued quickly it may be that the formula has cooled too much. Never force food into an unwilling chick's mouth as this may lead to aspiration and death.

Newly hatched or very weak chicks may not respond with strong pumping actions as do the older birds. Many will simply lick the food from the feeding instrument. In cases like these, the feeding process can be very slow and tedious. Usually this situation changes as the chick grows older or stronger.

In the larger species of birds the feeding response may become very strong and almost violent. Often the birds will lunge at the feeding instrument in an attempt to eat. Be careful not to injure birds during their excited solicitation to eat. The inside of the beak contains soft tissue that is easily lacerated by dull syringes or feeding tubes.

Chicks that have never been allowed to go hungry, but are fed continuously, may lose their feeding response. Many will open the esophagus and readily accept a full feeding of formula but they will never give any indication that they are willing to be fed. As they mature they may even pull their heads away, refusing to be fed, even if the formula is at the correct temperature. When this occurs it is necessary to skip a feeding or two and allow the chick to feel hunger. Many times this will force the chick to elicit the feeding response and it can once again be fed easily. It is not recommended that feedings be skipped on chicks that are not of excellent weight and health. The problem does not occur in all chicks and seldom, if ever, in those that are spoon fed. Babies that are ill and underweight should be force fed rather than be allowed to go hungry.

5.4 Temperature of the Food

The normal internal body temperature of a bird is between 101 and 103°F. Formula fed at these temperatures would be considered normal to the chick and is readily accepted. Unfortunately it is very difficult to maintain the formula at this temperature, get it into the syringes, and feed it to the chick before it has cooled enough to be refused by the bird. In order to avert this situation many aviculturists began to heat the formula a little higher before serving to see what would happen. They found that the chicks preferred the food a bit warmer and fed with more vigor. Through experimentation with different temperatures it was also discovered how high the limits were before the food caused damage to the bird's crop.

The maximum safety zone for feeding formula was established at 105 to 110°F. Anytime formula is fed at 100°F or below the chicks tend to refuse it. If it is fed higher than 110°F there is a possibility that some spots in the crop wall will be burned or damaged. Each chick has a preferred temperature at which it will feed best. Once that temperature zone is discovered it will be to the feeder's benefit to be consistent and always heat formula to this level.

Very young babies should be fed at the lower end of the range and the older, more finicky, birds at the higher end. Remember that if several birds are being fed at the same time, the temperature of the formula will fall while you are feeding. If the chicks seem to lose interest in feeding, recheck the temperature. If it has become cool to the touch or just barely warm enough, this could cause the problem. The food should be heated to the proper temperature before feeding is attempted again.

5.5 Consistency of the Formula

The consistency of the formula is very important. The proper consistency will vary depending on the age of the chick. It is also, in a small way, dependent on the feeding instrument that is to be used.

Chicks need a substantial amount of fluids in the first few days of life. This is why it is necessary to make the formula more watery than usual when feeding new hatches and very young birds. Many aviculturists who are feeding large quantities of birds like to draw off the watery layer that floats to the top of a bowl of the regular formula. This is thickened as each day goes on until regular consistency formula is being fed at about a week of age.

The proper consistency of regular formula is difficult to describe, but lies somewhere between heavy cream and apple sauce in thickness. If allowed to sit after preparation, formulas can thicken quite a bit. Water may need to be added before serving. The consistency used will depend on many factors. The first is the type of instrument being used to feed. Mixtures can be made thicker if a spoon is to be used, rather than a piston syringe. If the formula is too thick it may not flow through the end of a syringe. The next consideration is age or the stage of development of the chick. As important as very watery formula is for a chick in the first week, it can be dangerous when the chick gets older. A very young chick is easy to control, an older chick with a well-developed feeding response can get so enthusiastic about feeding that they can choke on a very watery formula. As a general rule, the thinner the formula the quicker it passes. When feeding thin formula you usually have to feed more often or in slightly increased quantity to make up for the extra water content. If the baby room is not air-conditioned and it is during the hot summer months, there may be a need to feed a thinner formula. The thinner formula will pass faster and may help compensate for the increased fluid requirements brought on by the hot weather. It may also help to speed the slowed digestion that can be caused by the heat. When feeding chicks in the last few weeks, just prior to weaning, and the room is air-conditioned, it is possible to feed a much thicker consistency. This is because a cool environment (not cold) speeds up the passage of food. The faster digestion may be physiologically necessary to provide the extra needed calories to keep the chick warm.

Before changing the consistency of the formula being fed, it is first necessary to evaluate how well the crop is moving and how the chick is developing. Barring other problems, an adjustment in consistency may sometimes put a bird back on the right track to proper digestion.

5.6 Quantity of Food

After the first week, the quantity of formula to be fed will be a function of many interdependent factors. It is at this time that the formula can be thickened. Thickening the formula makes it easier to stretch the crop because it is not so easily pushed up the esophagus causing aspiration. The amount that the crop expands will vary depending on the hand-feeder and the individual bird. Chicks of the same species and even chicks from the same clutch will grow at different rates and their crops will stretch at different rates. Individual chicks will also reach a different maximum crop capacity before weaning. In many ways the hand-feeder has a major influence on the maximum crop capacity.

Many aviculturists are reluctant to stretch the crops of young chicks while others push them to hold as much formula as possible. Those that choose to feed in smaller quantities must pay the price of feeding more often. The opposite is also true, some people prefer to stretch out the crop quickly so one of the daily feedings can be eliminated from their busy work schedule. Whatever the schedule, remember that it is as important not to under-feed in the second week of life as it is not to over-feed in the first week. The second week is a fast growth time and the chick needs adequate nutrition to grow properly. Caution must still be taken not to overstretch the crop and cause physical damage.

The indicator as to how much food a chick can hold in its crop is the esophageal canal on the side of the neck. It is wise to watch the right side of the neck where the esophagus meets the crop. The food will be visible in the neck as the crop reaches its full point. If the food is quickly emptied from the neck into the crop, more formula can be fed. Additional food can be fed until it is moving very slowly from the neck area into the crop. The crop is full when the last bit of food fed does not empty out of the esophageal canal. Always feed slowly and cautiously when the crop has reached this level of capacity. Ideally, food should extend up the neck no more than one half of the distance between the lower mandible and the top of the crop. If overfed, a small feeding tube can be used to remove a portion of the food. This procedure is explained in detail in the section titled *Emptying the crop.*

When a crop is properly filled it will feel taut to the touch. The same amount of formula should be fed for the following few feedings. At this point, the same quantity of food will not quite fill the crop completely. Once again the crop can be stretched to hold a bit more by using the same method described above.

The time period in which the crop empties tells whether increases were too sudden. For example, if it was taking four hours for the crop to empty and the increased quantity caused the crop to take six hours to empty, the increase may have been too much. Expansion of the crop capacity must be done slowly.

In the third week the maximum crop capacity may be reached on small species of birds. This means that the amounts being fed at each feeding will not increase substantially for the remainder of the hand-feeding process. The same point will not generally be reached on medium-sized birds until they are about six to eight weeks old. Some of the larger Macaws and very large Cockatoos may not reach the maximum quantities until eight to ten weeks.

The maximum quantities given will also depend on whether or not the chick is to be fed two or three times a day just prior to weaning. Those that are maintained on two feedings a day must accommodate a larger quantity than those treated to the extra feeding. The following list of quantities are approximate maximum crop capacities for certain species of birds. They are not to be interpreted as the rule. All birds are individuals and should be fed accordingly.

Species	Maximum Crop Capacity
Large Macaws	120-140 ml
Large Cockatoo	80-120 ml
Small Macaw	45-60 ml
Small Cockatoo	50-70 ml
Large Amazon	60-70 ml
Small Amazon	45-55 ml
Pionus/Small Amazons	30-40 ml
African Grey	50-60 ml
Mitred Conure	40-50 ml
Red-masked, Blue-Crowned and Nanday Conures	25-30 ml
Sun, Jenday, Gold-capped Conures	20-25 ml
Alexandrine and Derbyan Parakeets	20-30 ml
Ring-necked parakeets	12-20 ml
Pyrrhura Conures	12-20 ml
Cockatiels	12-15 ml
Brotogeris Parakeets	10-12 ml
Lovebirds	6-10 ml
Budgerigars	5-10 ml

5.7 Frequency of Feeding

The frequency at which a chick is fed is a function of two variables — the quantity fed, and the speed at which that food empties into the digestive system. The number of times the chick is fed will decrease after the first week due to the increasing volume of food that will be fed at each feeding. In the second and third week of life, the developmental changes that take place will occur at a rapid rate. It is during this time that the small, naked nestling begins its transformation into a parrot. The food (fuel) necessary to do this can be provided only through increased volumes of food, not through increased frequency of feeding. As the volume of food increases, the time required for the crop to empty increases and the frequency of feedings decreases. The normal progression from an every two hour schedule to an every three or four hour feeding schedule will be rapid. If a chick is not pushed to hold more formula but is instead fed less formula more frequently, it may never *take off* at the rapid growth rate of the babies that are pushed to hold more food. Caution is in order because the increased volumes must be attained without over-stretching the crop.

As the chick gets older and begins heavy feather growth, a reverse situation occurs. Older chicks seem to do better if fed smaller quantities more frequently. This is partially due to the fact that the crop will hold enough food to sustain the chick for, perhaps, twelve hours. The large quantity of formula can cause the crop to loose some of its elasticity and become less efficient. After the food remains in the crop for this great length of time it tends to sour. Decreasing the amount fed and increasing the frequency helps to eliminate these two problems. An eight hour period between feedings is recommended over a twelve hour period. This will reduce the amount of sour food the system has to digest and more food can be fed due to increased crop motility.

The increased frequency of feeding at this stage of development is advantageous for weight gain. Babies on the eight hour schedule can digest more food and thus will gain or maintain their weight better. For example, if a chick is fed 140ml of formula twice a day they will receive a 280ml total for that day. If the quantity is decreased to 110ml and is fed three times a day, the total increases to 330ml for the day. This is a total daily increase of almost 18% more food digested in a twenty-four hour period. Since the maximum growth period is already past, the increase does not make a critical difference. Babies fed either way will be large and healthy but those fed more food will tend to be healthier and more robust. It is always easier for a chick to enter into weaning with a few extra grams of body weight. Thinner chicks may need to be fed occasionally during weaning which may slow or even stop the weaning process.

5.8 How to Feed

How a chick is fed depends on the type of instrument that will be used. With only one exception, all feeding instruments require the feeder to manage the chick's head with their free hand.

Spoon feeding is a common and acceptable method to feed most young parrots. The method that is most comfortable is the one that should be used. When spoon feeding, the free hand is used to stabilize the head of the chick to be fed. In very small chicks this may mean only that the head of the chick is resting between the thumb and forefinger. As chicks get a little larger, the free hand is cupped around the back of the head or rested on the shoulders. If the chick's head needs to be elevated or restricted to keep it from flailing from side to side, a firmer grip may need to be applied.

Spoon feeding a baby bird is basically the same as spoon feeding a human baby. When dealing with birds that do not want to eat, it can be just as messy as feeding a child. The feel of the warm edges of the spoon or the warm formula in the mouth usually causes the chick to elicit a feeding response. When this does not occur, try placing the spoon further into the beak so that it touches the pressure pads or rubs on the inside of the upper beak. Once the response occurs, tilt the spoon in a manner that the formula flows into the mouth of the chick. This is done very slowly so the baby does not choke on the formula. The flow of food should be no more than the baby can swallow. If the mouth overflows with formula the risk of aspiration is the same as if the chick was being fed with a syringe or similar feeding instrument.

Spoon fed babies may wean easier than those that are syringe or tube fed. This is probably due to the fact that the chick actually tastes the food and feels it in the mouth. Chicks respond best to this method if it has been employed from a very young age. There are, however, two major drawbacks to this method. The first is that it will be the chick that decides how much it wishes to consume, not you. This is not a problem with those that feed readily and want more than they actually need. But, when dealing with babies that do not want to eat, and have not eaten enough, the outcome could be a thin or underfed bird. The second drawback is that spoon feeding is very time consuming. This makes it impractical when large quantities of babies need to be fed. Spoon feeding can be a messy experience. Inexperienced feeders may find that more food ends up on the chick than in the chick.

Properly controlling a chick's head while you elicit a feeding response can require a bit of skill. Too much pressure and the baby feels like it is being restrained. This usually results in a strong reaction to pull away. Not enough pressure and the chick is not being controlled. An uncontrolled bird can be very difficult to feed.

Proper restraint during feeding requires the use of all but one of the fingers on the free hand. As previously mentioned, the thumb and forefinger are used to activate the feeding response. This is usually accomplished by touching the corners or sides of the mouth with just the right amount of pressure. If you press too hard you will not only fail to get a feeding response but the chick may become frightened and pull away. Try keeping the fingers curved out away from the mouth of the chick so that only the finger tips are actually touching the corners of the mouth. This method is practiced because, for one, the parent birds only use the end of the beak to feed, and two, if you apply pressure with the entire finger you may cause damage to the eyes. The remaining fingers on the hand are used as a sort of a yoke to support the back of the head of the baby. Spread your fingers apart and apply minimal pressure to help keep the head in the upward position. If pressure is placed against the neck of the chick it may pinch off the entrance to the esophagus. Sometimes using the chick's jawbone to support the head is more comfortable. The proper position will be one where the head is stretched upwards and very slightly to the back. If the hands are positioned correctly you should have reasonable control of the chick and still be able to evoke a feeding response.

The next step is to feed the chick. If you are going to put the formula into the baby's mouth and allow it to swallow as you feed, it doesn't matter what instrument you use, the effect is the same as if you were spoon feeding. If you choose to use one of the faster methods to feed, the following information could

Using piston syringe to feed a Jendaya Conure.

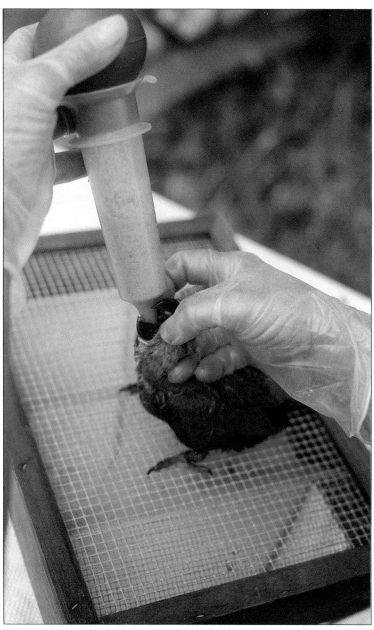

Feeding a Jendaya with a bulb syringe.

Feeding Macaw with a bulb syringe.

Spoon feeding a Macaw.

Tube feeding a Macaw.

The head should be tilted back, the neck extended and the syringe held straight up while feeding.

be very important. The entrance to the crop is called the esophagus. This entrance is a soft fleshy canal that normally runs down the right side of the bird's neck. This is an important point, it is the bird's right side, not your right side as you are facing the bird. The entrance to the esophagus is located at the inside rear of the bird's mouth. When facing the bird it will be slightly to your left, deep in the rear of the mouth. Since the beak is usually an obstacle to feeding, it is necessary to guide the feeding instrument into the beak from the bird's left side of the open beak, over the tongue to the right rear of the mouth in order to direct the flow of food towards the crop entrance. Remember to elevate the head and stretch the neck upwards while tilting the head backwards a bit. This will help tremendously in directing the food into the proper place. Keep the syringe or feeding instrument in the vertical position rather than horizontal while feeding.

Catheter or tube feeding is done in the same way. The tube is slipped into the mouth on the bird's left side. It passes over the tongue and into the esophagus to the crop. This procedure is explained in more detail in the following section on force feeding.

Power or rapid feeding of chicks is a common practice among aviculturists who feed numerous chicks. During the pumping motion of the head a baby parrot opens the esophagus and has no need to swallow every mouthful of formula. This makes it possible, with the use of a syringe or some instrument that can project the food, to inject large quantities of food into the crop without the bird having to swallow. This is a natural physical ability for the young parrots. It is not so natural for people and becomes a side show if one is capable of doing it while *chugging* a pitcher of beer. The most important thing to remember is to stop delivery of the food if it backs up into the mouth. Allow the chick to clear its mouth before beginning to feed again. There will also be times when no matter how fast you feed, the food does not back up but continues to go directly into the crop. This is when the chick has opened its esophagus. With a little practice you will learn to recognize these moments and can take advantage of the situation by feeding very rapidly.

In establishments where large quantities of chicks need to be fed at the same time, power feeding will be absolutely necessary. The moment the chick opens its esophagus the food is delivered with a powerful push of the syringe. If the chick's head is tilted back, the neck is properly stretched, and the syringe is in the vertical position, the force of the directed formula will keep the esophagus open long enough to deliver about 60 milliliters of formula in one shot. This method should not be used unless the feeder is extremely competent at feeding by the other methods mentioned and there is a need to feed rapidly. One of the drawbacks of this feeding method is a possible weaning problem due to the lack of feeding satisfaction of the chick. The food is delivered so quickly that often the chick does not realize that it has been fed. Another potential problem would be the lack of bonding between feeder and parrot. This is true in situations where the feeder quickly passes to the next chick and spends no time with each individual. The more time that is spent interacting with the chicks, the tamer and more bonded they will become.

5.9 Force Feeding (When a chick will not eat)

Chicks that are imprinted on their parents and are pulled from the nest to be hand-fed may refuse to eat for the new human feeder. These chicks must be fed with extreme caution or they may aspirate food and die. Aspiration becomes more of a risk with chicks that roll over on to their backs in a natural defense posture. There are also risks involved with feeding weak or debilitated chicks that elicit no feeding response. A working solution to both of these problems is to force feed them until they become accustomed to human companionship.

Force feeding is accomplished with some type of feeding tube, catheter, or gavage tool. Metal gavage needles become lethal weapons in the hands of the inexperienced and should be used only by those that are proficient at restraint and force feeding of birds. In most cases it is safer and more highly recommended that a rubber tube be used. Even a soft rubber tube can be dangerous if used improperly. Most rubber tubes will begin to harden with age and constant disinfection. When these tubes become inflexible and rigid, they are as dangerous as a metal gavage needle. On the other hand, new, soft rubber tubes are so flexible that they are often difficult to guide into the right direction when trying to enter the crop. In practice, rubber tubes that are used but not hard and rigid suit the purpose in the best way.

Sizing of the feeding instrument is very important. Very small chicks cannot accommodate tubes or gavages that are thicker than the opening of the esophagus. Experienced aviculturists use a variety of instruments like aquarium tubing, urethral catheters, or puppy feeding tubes. The length of the tube is also important but will actually depend on what is comfortable for the feeder. It is a good practice to compute the required length by adding three or four inches to the length measured from the tip of the beak down the side of the neck to the center of the crop. In this way it is easy to assess where the tip of the tube is by allowing the extra length to extend out of the bird's beak when feeding. The longer the feeding tube, the less control the feeder has. Be sure not to cut the tube so short that it will disappear into the crop of the chick if it should accidentally slip off of the end of the syringe. Retrieving a short tube from the crop of a chick is not always an easy task. If an accident does occur, consult chapter 10 section 2 for advice.

Any object that is to be inserted into the crop of a chick must be blunted on the end to avoid injury. Most metal gavage needles available today have a smooth round ball on the end for safe insertion. Rubber catheter tubes that are shortened for feeding will need to be filed with an emery board or flame smoothed with a match. This will eliminate any sharp edges on the rubber that may cause injury. Care must be taken not to force the end of the tube into the crop wall. This may cause bruising or even a crop puncture. These injuries can cause regurgitation due to discomfort.

The hand posture that is used to manage a bird during voluntary hand-feeding is the same that is used to force feed. The only difference is in the amount of pressure that is applied by the hand that is on the bird. The thumb and forefinger, that are normally used to elicit the feeding response of the chick, are placed a little more forward where pressure can be placed directly on the space between the upper and lower mandible. This pressure should force the unwilling chick to open its beak. Ideally the pressure must be maintained throughout the procedure to prevent the chick from closing the beak and pinching off the flow of the food. Once the chick is in position, the tube is carefully guided over the tongue and into the entrance to the esophagus. Never force a tube down the throat of the chick. It should enter the crop, through the esophagus, with no resistance. This procedure is best performed by two people. One can restrain the chick while the other inserts the tube and uses their free hand to feel exactly where the end of the tube has gone. If you have any doubt as to whether or not the tube is in the crop, simply wiggle the tube to see if there is any movement in the crop area.

The inexperienced feeder may mistake the trachea (windpipe) for the feeding tube. They feel very much the same when touched from the outside of the neck. By sliding the tube up and down a little bit one can tell which is which. The trachea will not move up and down, only side to side. When performing this procedure for the first time it is always wise to employ an assistant. With experience, it can be done easily by one person. Never be in a rush as this often leads to disaster.

Healthy chicks that are pulled from the nest may try to resist feeding by flipping onto their backs. The feeder must restrain these chicks from doing so while stretching the neck of the chick. This can be accomplished by gently pulling up on the head of the chick while resting the wrist of the same hand on the chick's back. Continue this restraint until the tube has been withdrawn from the crop.

Dry tubes or feeding gavages are difficult to insert into the esophagus. For this reason it is recommended that some type of lubricant be used so the tube will slip easily through the esophageal opening. *Ky Jelly,* spray type cooking oils, warm water or even a bit of formula will work well as a lubricant.

Aspiration of chicks is still very possible when using tubes or gavage type feeding instruments. The most common mistake that is made is when the tube is not inserted far enough into the crop and the food backs up and is forced up through the esophagus and into the mouth. Anytime food is noticed in the mouth the tube must be withdrawn and the chick released immediately. For some reason, chicks will not cough or try to clear the throat if they are restrained. This leads to inhalation of the formula and either pneumonia or death. The same scenario applies when too much food is placed into the crop causing it to overflow into the mouth.

The capacity of the crop should always be evaluated before any chick is force fed. Parent fed chicks tend to have a larger feeding capacity because they have been fed solid foods. This is not always true. It has been noticed that African Grey chicks will often have a much smaller crop capacity if fed by the parents as opposed to those that are being hand-reared on liquid formula. The crop capacity of parent fed chicks will vary depending on the attitude of the parent birds that have fed them.

The only difference between tube feeding and force feeding is the amount of force that must be used to open the beak and restrain the chick. When dealing with a reluctant feeder, force feeding becomes tube feeding when the chick stops resisting the tube and feeds voluntarily. At this point, a decision must be made as to whether to continue to tube feed or switch to another method.

Moluccan Cockatoo — 10 days (*Cacatua moluccensis*)

Moluccan Cockatoo — 25 days (*Cacatua moluccensis*)

Moluccan Cockatoo — 35 days (*Cacatua moluccensis*)

Moluccan Cockatoo — 45 days (*Cacatua moluccensis*)

Blue and Gold Macaw 1 week (*Ara ararauna*)

Blue and Gold Macaw 3 weeks (*Ara ararauna*)

Blue and Gold Macaw 5 weeks (*Ara ararauna*)

Blue and Gold Macaw 7 weeks (*Ara ararauna*)

Blue and Gold Macaw 8 weeks (*Ara ararauna*)

Blue and Gold Macaw 9 weeks (*Ara ararauna*)

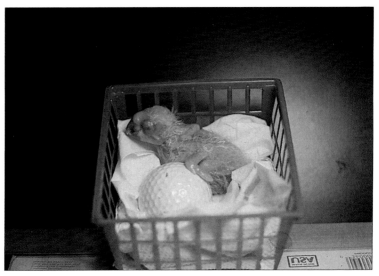

Yellow Collared Macaw 1 wk. (*Ara auricollis*)

Yellow Collared Macaw 3 weeks (*Ara auricollis*)

Yellow Collared Macaw 5 weeks (*Ara auricollis*)

Yellow Collared Macaw 6 weeks (*Ara auricollis*)

Yellow Collared Macaw 7 weeks (*Ara auricollis*)

Yellow Collared Macaw 8 weeks (*Ara auricollis*)

Green Conure 1 week (*Aratinga holochlora*)

Green Conure 3 weeks (*Aratinga holochlora*)

Green Conure 4 weeks (*Aratinga holochlora*)

Green Conure 5 weeks (*Aratinga holochlora*)

Green Conure 6 weeks (*Aratinga holochlora*)

Green Conure 7 weeks (*Aratinga holochlora*)

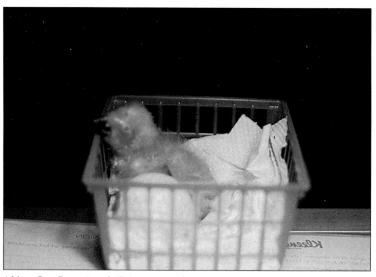

African Grey Parrot 1 week (*Psittacus e. erithacus*)

African Grey Parrot 3 weeks (*Psittacus e. erithacus*)

African Grey Parrot 5 weeks (*Psittacus e. erithacus*)

African Grey Parrot 6 weeks (*Psittacus e. erithacus*)

African Grey Parrot 7 weeks (*Psittacus e. erithacus*)

African Grey Parrot 8 weeks (*Psittacus e. erithacus*)

Chapter 6
Weight Monitoring

6.1 General

Systematic weight monitoring of parrot chicks is a necessity. The majority of problems encountered in the nursery will be represented by sudden weight loss. Even the failure to gain weight in young chicks during a twenty-four hour period can be interpreted as a possible warning sign that illness may be imminent.

Health and weight assessment of one or two chicks that have been purchased as pets can be performed through physical examination. However, if large numbers of chicks are to be raised, a gram scale will have to be purchased for this purpose. Gram scales do not need to be highly accurate, to the fraction of a gram, but they should be consistent. Consistency can be measured by weighing several objects of different weights. Weigh these things several times, to assure the scales always display the same weight for each object. The consistent measure of a scale is important when weighing parrot chicks.

Chicks should be weighed when the crop is completely empty. Ideally the crop should be so empty that it appears to be indented. The reason for this is that hand feeding formulas are very heavy. The approximate weight is one gram per milliliter. If there are substantial amounts of formula in the crop the recorded weight can be very erroneous.

6.2 Daily Weight Gains (What is Normal?)

Normal or *correct* weights for a particular species of parrot chick, at a given stage in development, can be highly variable. A few of the influencing factors are the growth rate at which it is developing and the weight at which it hatched. To a certain degree, genetics plays a role in the potential size that the chick will obtain.

Many of the sample weight charts and growth charts that have been previously published are limited in their use. This is because most of them fail to state the scientific controls under which the weights were obtained. Were the chicks weighed at the same time each day? Were they completely empty of formula? Had the chicks been fed by the parents and for how long? All of these things influence the normal weight for a chick at a given age. Without this information the recorded weights are useless if they are to be compared to other hand-feeding chicks. Any one of these controls can mean a major difference in what weight could be considered normal.

In the past there has also been a fair amount of misreporting of baby weights. For whatever reason, some babies are purposely weighed with partially full crops and in other cases the weights of parent fed babies are presented as hand-fed weights. These reports also failed to state at what age the chick was taken from the parents or if it was raised by hand from hatching. A three-week-old Macaw that was fed by hand since hatch will rarely weigh anywhere near as much as a three-week-old Macaw that was left with the parents for the first two weeks. Unfortunately, in each case the baby's weight is reported as that of a normal hand-feeding three-week-old with no further clarification. This information can be misleading and discouraging to the novice who cannot under-stand why their chicks weigh so much less than the reflected records. It is highly advisable to be more concerned with the overall health and growth rather than the weight comparisons between hand-fed babies that someone else is raising. The important thing to remember is that the same type of birds can be developing normally but at different rates. As long as the chick is in good color, shows signs of good hydration, maintains a rounded breast, and weighs more than the previous day, you can be reasonably sure it is developing normally.

After several years of weight monitoring it is our experience that almost all medium to large parrots have the same growth pattern in the first two to three weeks of development. Records kept on our babies as well as reliable records from other sources revealed that if all controllable variables are the same, a Macaw, Cockatoo, Amazon, or African Grey will exhibit the same growth rate. The smaller species of parrots and parakeets have not been studied here but it would be surprising if these patterns were different for smaller birds.

After the realization that most weight charts were worthless when trying to determine whether a chick was developing normally, we researched a few other possible monitoring techniques. It was discovered that if the hatch weight, age, and current weight are known, it is possible to plot when a chick should double its weight and on what incremental basis this would continue. If these *normal growth* patterns prove to be reliable, as they seem to be, this information would be much more valuable than weights of chicks that someone else has raised. The most surprising fact was that all of the species being compared fit into the exact same parameters. The only major variation noticed was when growth was monitored using different formulas, not different species. Growth patterns vary in the amount of time required for each weight doubling. This variability can be attributed to the use of a rapid hydration type formula versus a watered down version of the standard monkey chow formula. It can be further noted that these differences only occur dependent on which food is used in the first four or five days of life (see section 5.2).

Chicks that were fed on the rapid hydration formula doubled their hatch weights in three to five days. This weight again doubled between days seven and nine and a third doubling took place between days eleven and fourteen. Those that were fed the thinned monkey biscuit formula doubled their hatch weights at between five and six and a half days of age. The second doubling took place between ten and twelve and one half days and a third doubling was between day seventeen and day nineteen. To simplify this a bit, take for example, a baby Macaw that hatches at eighteen grams. It should weigh 144 grams at the age of ten to twelve days if it is fed on the hydration formula. If it is fed a watered down version of the monkey biscuit formula it will reach 144 grams between seventeen and nineteen days. This number is eight times the original hatch weight. If you are feeding a chick that is a day behind this schedule there is not cause for alarm. If it should fall behind by more than one day there may be something lacking in either the brooding, diet, or the way it is being fed. Chicks that become ill will not attain the doubled weights on the days specified. Anytime a baby is sick it will fall behind in development.

The physical examination of the chick is far more important than actual weight data. It must be remembered that if a baby does not meet one of the weight doubling goals, it probably will not catch up and make the next. As long as the chick appears to be healthy and does not get too thin, there is little cause for alarm. Many chicks develop at a different rate for unexplainable reasons. This does not mean that they will not grow up to be healthy normal birds.

6.3 What Influences Weight Fluctuations?

Some aviculturists assume that a healthy normal developing baby parrot should always gain as much or more weight than the day before. This is not the case. If you chart a baby's daily weight gain rather than daily total weight, several interesting facts will be revealed. Although well-maintained and healthy babies should always show some weight gain from one day to the next, the amount of weight gained will fluctuate. A baby that gains fifteen grams one day can, in the normal course of development, gain eight grams the following day and eighteen grams the next. It may be difficult for some to believe this because the chick is digesting as much or more food than the day before. The truth is that parrot chicks, just as human children, tend to grow in spurts. If properly documented, it is actually normal for a baby parrot to have a day or two of decreased weight gain between each growth spurt. This does not mean that the chick loses weight, only that the amounts gained each day are lower. Then, suddenly, the actual weight gain increases once more. The causes for these growth spurts are unknown so this is certainly a subject that warrants further study.

Unlike these growth spurts, many weight gain variations are easily explainable. One of the common causes of fluctuations in weight gain is the amount of water that is used to make the formula. An increase or decrease in the amount of water in the formula can make a great difference. If the chick is in need of some hydration and extra water is available in the formula, you may notice an increase in weight gains even though the measured amount of food did not change. If a chick is well hydrated and extra water is mixed into the formula, a lower weight gain can be expected.

Something that is rarely considered is the amount of food that is still in the lower digestive tract when a baby is weighed. Even if the crop is completely empty there will be a difference in weight between a chick with food in the lower gut and one that has had time to empty the lower tract. It is normal for digestion to increase the speed in which a specific volume of formula is passed. In other words, in as little as one day's growth, a chick may digest food and excrete droppings at a faster rate. The larger the chick, the more substantial the difference in weight may be. The expulsion of one dropping from a large Macaw baby can weigh five or ten grams. The weight of the contents of the entire lower digestive system can be very significant.

As chicks get older and near the full grown stage of development, daily weight gains decrease. This occurs even though the amount of formula digested may increase. In addition, there are several other factors that influence weight gains but are totally independent of dietary factors. These are discussed in the following chapter.

6.4 Record Keeping

Weights and daily weight gains are invaluable information about the chicks being reared. By plotting daily information, health assessment is easier if one has no experience in hand-rearing. Remember that the overall general health and appearance of the chick is always more important than how much it weighs on a certain day at a certain age. It is difficult to convince some that, due to the variability in developmental processes between chicks, weight charts are of a lesser importance than health status. It is true that most healthy chicks will fall into a certain weight parameter for their age, but to say that they should weigh the same at a given number of days of age is bogus. This weight comparison practice may have been started when feeding formulas were being tested and aviculturists were trying to establish which one worked better. In any case, adult weights vary and so do those of the chicks. This natural occurrence makes the determination of proper weights per species virtually impossible to define. Adjustments are continually being made in the wild. If two birds, that are small for their species, breed and produce young, these chicks will not necessarily be small. As a matter of fact, many times the siblings outgrow the parent birds before they leave the nest.

It is the variability, not the consistency in normal weights that make record keeping so important for the commercial breeder. If the information plotted on siblings of a certain pair were always the same, there would be no need to record them and nothing would ever be learned from them. It is impossible to know what is *normal* if we cannot define what is *abnormal*.

Keeping weight charts or graphs is a time consuming chore. The daily recording of weights should be made as easy as possible so the keeper will not abandon the project. When designing a weight record for chicks, the easiest way is to use a column form log. Across the top of the form, in each column, list the information that is desired. Important information could include the date, age of the chick, weight for that day, time of day, hatch weight, actual weight gain or loss from the previous day, amount of formula fed the day prior, and a note as to whether the crop is completely empty or not. Each chick should have a form that contains the necessary information to trace its lineage. After chicks are banded, the numbers should also be recorded to assist in easy identification.

Design a regime that is comfortable. If the system is too difficult or time consuming it will be postponed during busy times. Once a record contains several days of blank spaces, it will become useless. It is important to be consistent and record all pertinent data regardless of how long it may take.

A filing system of baby records must also be established in a commercial operation. It is usually easy to file, by the year, records and band number of chicks that have been reared. If data is required on a certain chick, all that is needed is the band number to find the information. A small, cross-reference card file can be maintained by species. In this way it will be possible to find a record on a certain species of bird. For example, if a record is needed for a Goffin's Cockatoo that was reared three years ago, locate the file card under Goffin's Cockatoos, find the card with the listed band numbers, and search for the files by band number. This complete system will eliminate the need to pull records based totally on memory.

6.5 The Physical Exam for Weight

Weight monitoring may tell you what a chick weighs, but this information is limited in its use. It is more important to know if a chick is in *good weight* for its body size. As previously mentioned, there is no correct weight for a particular type of chick at any given stage of development. Averages, graphs, or sample weights may give you an idea if your chick is comparable to others of that species, but it still does not tell you if that particular chick is of a healthy weight for its structural size. A physical examination of the chick will reveal more useful information than any weight data.

The breast muscle of the chick is the most important area of examination. First locate the keel of the breast. This is the bone-like line that runs up the middle of the breast. The breast muscles are attached to both sides of the keel. Ideally they should be well rounded with no indentations. If you draw a line from the left side of the chick, over the keel and across the right side, it should look like a U not a V. If the breast is not plump and rounded, the line will tend to be very sharp at the keel giving it the appearance of the letter V. Thin babies do not necessarily indicate the presence of a disease but the possibility should not be ignored.

There are numerous reasons that a chick might be a little underweight. The formula may be deficient in fat content or the feeder may not have fed the chick properly. The importance of well-rounded, heavy babies is that they are less likely to be harboring some type of disease factor. Additional weight also provides the chick with a *cushion* should it eventually require some form of treatment.

If the breast muscle is emaciated, there is cause for alarm. Whenever the muscle is so small that you can feel the sides of the keel and a large indented muscle area, there is usually some type of degenerative disease factor involved. Babies in this condition should be examined by an avian veterinarian and cultures should be taken. The causative agent may be something very simple like a minor bacterial infection. These are easily treatable and the chick should begin to gain weight as therapy begins. The keel area and the breast muscle is an important inspection site for adult parrots as well. When birds lose considerable amounts of weight in this area it should be considered as a sign of illness.

In very young babies that have not been well-hydrated from the first day, the chest will appear a bit thin. As said before, it is extremely difficult and sometimes impossible to correct this deficit, especially when a rapid growth pattern has been set. What occurs is that the chick grows at a faster rate than the fat and nutrients can supply, thus the breast muscle remains thin. In cases like this you might wish to know if it's an ongoing problem or something that has been rectified. Since the breast might not change after the chick gets back on the right track, one must find another method to assess the situation. The bird's elbow or first joint down from the shoulder on the wing can reveal whether or not the chick is thin. If this area is full and plump, the baby is doing well despite the fact that the breast

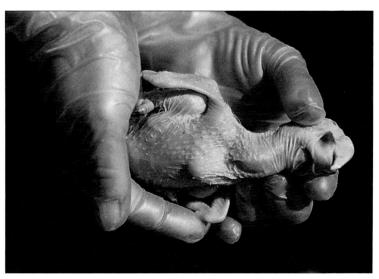

Healthy chick exhibiting full, rounded chest.

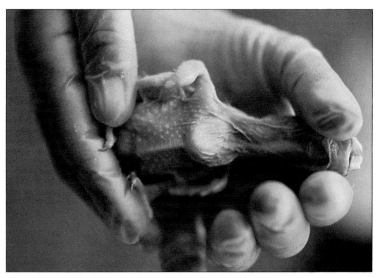

Slim chick exhibiting V-shaped chest with prominent keel bone.

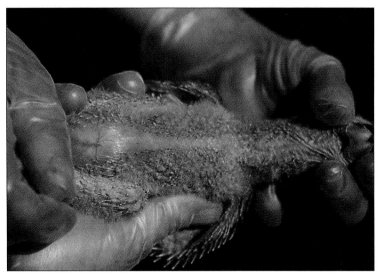

Ideally, a chick should be heavy and well-rounded.

Inspection of breast area for weight examination.

is a bit thin. When the elbow is thin or boney the chick has not yet begun to recover.

The chest and breast of very young chicks may appear thin due to under hydration in the first few days of life. If the chick is not hydrated properly, the deficit is very difficult or impossible to make up. What occurs is the chick grows at a more rapid pattern than the fat and nutrients can supply, thus the breast muscle remains thin. Since this scenario has an explanation, it can be assumed that the chick is not suffering from a bacterial or health problem. Another area of inspection that may help to make the determination of health is to inspect the elbow area. Even though parrots do not have elbows, *per se*, the second joint on the wing is often referred to as this. If the elbow area is plump and fleshy, the chick is probably healthy and is beginning to turn around from the past hydration problem.

Chapter 7
Non-Dietary Factors That Control Weight Gain

Although diet obviously plays the major role in determining how fast a baby parrot grows, there are many other factors that have an important influence. Birds that have grown to the same size, in the same period of time and on the same diet, can have drastically different weights. This can be noticed if weight records from several different aviculturists are compared. These weight differences are highly influenced by the environmental conditions in which the baby is raised as well as the condition of the crop. When negative environmental factors or poor crop condition start to become extreme, we see a slowing of growth, stunting syndrome, or death. Of course genetic differences will play a major role in determining how big the chick will be when full-grown but genes play a relatively minor role, compared to environmental factors and crop condition, in determining how heavy a chick will be, for its size, at any given stage of development.

It is always advantageous to keep the crop in top condition. The environmental conditions, however, can be manipulated to give a desired end result. An Amazon or Macaw can never be too fat for the pet industry. The ability to lose weight from stress without an adverse effect on the health of the bird is a must. If, however, you are raising babies in order to hold them back for future breeding you can afford to have a much thinner chick.

7.1 The Crop

The crop is technically a dilation of the esophagus that has a layer of muscular tissue within the walls. The crop, in effect, is a holding tank for food. It is important to realize that you do not feed the baby, you fill the crop and the crop feeds the baby. If this holding tank is kept in good condition it will function properly, if not, it can cause great problems or even death.

The muscular tissue within the walls of the crop is what causes the crop to contract and undulate. This contraction and undulation causes a downward pressure that helps to push the food down through the digestive system. As long as this muscular wall does not lose its elasticity it will keep pushing the food out of the crop and down through the system. When the crop is full, the pressure is at its greatest and food passage and digestion is rapid. This is one of the reasons that parent fed babies are so heavy.

After the first few days of life, conscientious parents will fill the baby's crop in the morning and keep it full all day long. The constant, increased pressure from a crop that is always packed to the limit keeps the food passing through the digestive tract at a much more rapid rate than if the crop were maintained at only half-full. This cannot be mimicked during hand feeding for several reasons. First there is the problem of consistency. the parent birds feed diced or chopped seeds, fruits and vegetables, and sufficient water. A mixture like this, when left to stand for several hours, actually becomes more nutritious and digestible as the time passes, especially if it contains a fair amount of dry seed and nut meats. It is, in fact, changing from dry seed to a soaked, more hydrated seed and soaked seed is always higher in nutritional value.

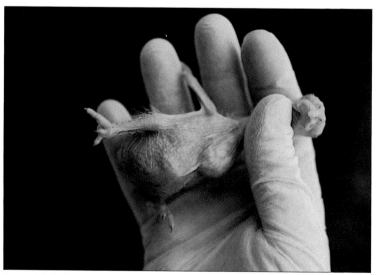

Parent fed chick showing "chunky" crop contents and normally enlarged abdomen with definition.

Examining the crop contents of Amazons and Conures taken out of their nests in Central America proved very interesting. Not only did the crop appear to be over-filled, but the contents were made up of about ninety percent seed, both dry and green. The remaining ten percent was unidentifiable green plant material. Hand feeding formulas on the other hand are always saturated with water before they are fed. Once a foodstuff becomes saturated with water it immediately begins to sour and grow bacteria. The more sour the food the slower it moves through the crop and this slows digestion and weight gain. For this reason one cannot continually feed on top of old food in order to keep the crop full. You must let it empty periodically in order to keep the bacterial levels from becoming dangerously high. The truth is that parent fed birds are almost always digesting wholesome fresh or soaked seeds or vegetables and the hand fed bird is almost always digesting *soured mush*. This is the reason why monkey chow based formulas should always be boiled prior to serving and all prepared powdered mixes are sterilized sometime during the manufacturing process. This substantially slows down but does not eliminate the bacterial build-up which causes the souring.

Experiments were done in Honduras during commercial hand-rearing of Yellow-naped Amazons. We were not in a position to boil and rapid cool the formula for 500 Amazons in order to slow down souring. Therefore, all birds were allowed to empty completely between every feeding. It was a monumental task trying to regulate the feeding so that all 500 birds were all empty at one time.

Experimentation with antibiotics in the formula to control the bacterial growth was accomplished. We hoped that this would allow us to feed on top of old food during the day, then our main concern would be the birds being completely empty in the morning. The antibiotic chosen was tetracycline and it worked great. We continually fed on top of old food and worried only about the babies being empty once a day. There was no instance of sour crop and all the babies were fatter than usual.

We thought we had found an excellent substitute for the boiling and rapid cooling method of sterilization on our domestic harvest, this, however, did not prove to be true. Even though all the Amazons and African Greys came out nice and fat, all the Macaws and Conures ended up dangerously thin and completely unsalable. We terminated the use of the tetracycline and supplemented them with raw goat's milk (lactobacillus); the weight gains began to skyrocket. Apparently the lack of the proper bacterial flora in the digestive tract is of much greater significance in Macaws and Conures than in Amazons and African Greys.

The second reason that this cannot be mimicked when hand feeding is the fact that hand-feeding formulas, being saturated with water, are approximately 40% heavier than a parent fed diet. This extra weight can easily cause the crops' muscular walls to lose their elasticity if they are continually filled to the maximum as the parents would do. This loss of elasticity in the walls of the crop causes a sagging crop that will never completely empty. This always leads to the condition known as sour crop which is usually followed by poor weight gain and bacterial infection.

The way to avoid these problems is to feed less food more frequently. If the crop is never stretched then it will remain relatively small and it will hold less food when tightly filled. As the chick gets older, rather than stretching the crop in order to cut the number of feedings from every four hours to every twelve hours, the crop can be stretched less as the baby reaches the age where it will be taking its maximum volume of food during the hand-feeding process. In other words, crops that could be stretched to hold twelve hours of formula are stretched enough to hold only eight hours of food. This will maintain maximum pressure with a minimum amount of food. This method will yield babies that are much heavier than those that are stretched to the point that they can be fed twice a day. Digestion is also aided by the fact that with less food in the crop it empties faster and is constantly replenished with fresh food that passes more rapidly and is digested more efficiently. Unfortunately this is not always possible with birds that are destined for the pet trade. These birds must have their crops stretched to the point that they have only to be fed two or three times a day, otherwise the shopkeeper would have time for little else other than hand-feeding.

7.2 Lighting and Space

Most aviculturists do not realize that lighting and brooder space have a major effect on the weight of the chicks. Nature's intent is to grow a bird as fast as possible and this is accomplished in their natural habitat in a dark area with highly restricted space.

In fact the chick receives little or no visual stimulation and is able to engage in only extremely limited movement. This is not only due to the limited amount of space that exists in the nesting hollows but also because the lack of visual stimulation causes a lack of interest in moving around.

The fact is, if all a chick does is lay motionless and digest food, it cannot help but gain weight. This is what nature intended and this is how chicks grow best. This might not, however, be the best way to raise a chick for pet purposes. Chicks that are raised in a spacious brooder with plenty of light and other companions lose a lot of weight from increased activity. In an experiment that we did in Honduras with Yellow-naped Amazons, I discovered just how important space and lighting can be. On a buying trip to the interior, I refused a clutch of three baby birds because they were too young (1 to 4 days old) to handle the stress of traveling with me until I reached the holding facility. I promised that if they were fat and healthy when I returned in several weeks, I would be glad to take them. I was not very hopeful because all they were being fed was ground corn, red beans and water. I, unfortunately, did not have enough spare monkey biscuits to leave for hand-feeding.

When I returned three weeks later, I was brought into a dark room and the birds were presented to me in a small soap carton. It was bursting with three of the healthiest and fattest baby

Typical abdomen of parent fed chick in "natural" nesting conditions.

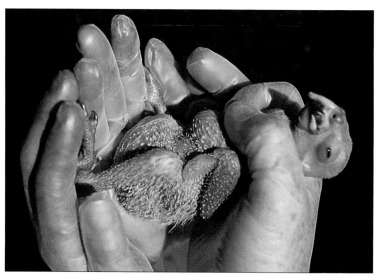

Chicks confined to small dark brooding areas will develop abdominal shape similar to parent fed chicks.

Smooth less protruding abdomen of active hand-fed chick, brooded in spacious well lit containers.

Yellow-Napes that I had ever seen. They were far heavier than anything that I had raised on all of my fancy imported scientifically correct diets. After the initial shock, I realized that the diet could not possibly be better than what I was using, so I began to think about other possibilities.

It had to be the environment in which the birds were raised. Our birds, at our holding facility, were being raised in large well-lit cartons or corrals. Some of the larger corrals held as many as thirty birds. There was always plenty of room and although they slept most of the time, they did run around and play with each other. It seemed, the larger the groups, the more playing occurred. There was always one or two birds running around waking everyone else up.

The other Napes were raised with only three in a box that was very small and kept in a totally dark place. At that point I decided to begin my experiment as soon as more babies became available.

The following week a trapper brought me three clutches of week-old Napes. Each clutch consisted of two chicks. I took one chick from each of the three clutches and placed them in a small box in a dark but well-ventilated closet. I marked the other three and placed them in one of our large well-lit boxes with about a dozen other birds. Both groups were fed the same diet with the same frequency and volume.

After three weeks, the difference between the two groups was incredible. The three in the carton weighed approximately 50% more than their three siblings raised in the larger groups. They not only were heavier but they had the oversized abdomens that are seen in parent fed babies. I had always assumed that the oversized abdomen shrunk because the babies were switched to a mushier diet. It now seemed obvious that the abdomens shrunk because of movement and not because of dietary change. I am not sure how much the oversized abdomens of the confined babies contributed to their overall propensity to gain weight. The fact that these babies were bigger and heavier, in every way, was obviously caused by several different effects of their environment. The darkness creating a stress-free environment was certainly a factor. The lack of movement, however, was probably the major factor.

What I have yet to determine is whether the lack of movement, in itself, was the major determining factor because it represented less of a calorie drain. Could it have been the fact that the lack of movement allowed the abdomen to remain large and digestion is more efficient when the abdomen and digestive tract is larger in relation to body size? Although I never lost any birds in this physical condition and therefore was not able to examine the abdomens internally, it was obvious from external examination that the increased abdomen size was due to the fact that the digestive organs were of larger size. They are also firm and have definition as opposed to being soft with fluids or bloated tight like a balloon as in some disease processes.

There was also a negative side to keeping the birds confined and in the dark. Their motor skills and personality development were far behind the chicks that were kept in the well lit, spacious brooder boxes. They were in general, very shy and inactive. This is a negative factor when one wishes the birds to be sold in the pinfeather stage to the pet trade. The babies in the large well lit boxes were active, playful and came running when they saw anyone approach. It also seemed that they were voraciously hungry more often. This is probably due to the calorie drain from activity which makes hand feeding by even a novice an easy chore. Taking all things into account, I would suggest trying to achieve a happy median between the two extremes.

The heavier chunkier baby had a large safety margin of body fat and muscle that allowed it to lose weight from stressful conditions including bacterial infections. This is an important factor in determining which birds survive a disease outbreak long enough to effect a cure. The slim babies will usually succumb immediately to the stress of the weight loss.

7.3 Temperature

How far above or below the optimum temperature, at which you set your brooder, will have an affect on how rapidly the formula passes out of the crop, since either of the extremes can slow food passage to a crawl. This, in turn, will have a drastic affect on weight gain and growth. The optimum temperature varies with the chick and the circumstances under which it was raised. One must be careful not to keep younger birds too cool and older babies too hot. In many climates it is beneficial to keep well pinfeathered babies in air-conditioned rooms (78 to 80°F). Monitoring the weight gains of a Buffon's Macaw on a twelve-hour basis had an interesting result.

The daytime high was about 90°F and nighttime temperatures ranged from 75 to 78°F. From 11:00 AM to 11:00 PM the weight gain was 2 grams. From 11:00 PM to 11:00 AM the weight gain was 15 grams. I installed an air-conditioner in the room which lowered the daytime temperature to about 80°F. The nighttime temperature remained the same. The daytime weight gain went up immediately to 8 grams and the night gains remained at 15 grams. This particular bird was not suffering from slow food passage and digested the same amount of food during the day as it did at night. The remaining difference in the weight gain was due to the fact that the bird was usually awake and active during the day and almost always asleep and motionless during the darkness of night. What I am not sure of is whether the poor weight gain in the overly hot room was caused by the bird dehydrating during the heat of the day and utilizing its weight gain or whether it was caused by the bird digesting less effectively due to the heat. We see a similar problem with very young chicks that are kept too cool. Again, I am not sure whether they do not have reasonable weight gains because they are burning up too much energy to keep warm or because they cannot metabolize efficiently when they are too cold. Determining optimum temperature at each stage of development to insure maximum weight gain is a study that would have great value.

7.4 Humidity

If the relative humidity remains between 50 and 75 percent, its effect on weight is almost non-existent. When the humidity dips much below this, dehydration can occur. The dehydration will slow the growth and weight gains of the chick. Humidity also has a major effect on the growth of feathers and the development of the body. Premature feathering, at the expense of size and development, can be forced by continually wetting chicks or exposing them to direct moisture. The result will be a bird that is moderately to severely undersized. For some reason, moisture causes the utilization of proteins and calcium to be directed to the production of feathers rather than skeletal and muscular structure. The feathers that are produced during this premature development are usually perfectly structured with no signs of stress bars or discolored areas.

In Honduras, where the price of feathered nestlings exceeds that of naked ones, the natives use this fact to cause premature feathering. They have learned that by bathing naked babies they can stimulate the feathers to grow several weeks early and they are able to sell these chicks at a higher price. The chicks are almost always undersized, sometimes severely, but the feathering is perfect. The natives are making use of a little known natural mechanism which allows the chicks to feather and fledge early if the rainy season comes early. Birds caught in the nest when the rains begin will drown so this saves the lives of many late hatches in the wild.

Humidity levels on the low end of acceptable seem to have an effect that is slightly opposite. The chicks will often feather a little later than normal. Dry skin is another symptom of low humidity brooding but this seems to have no effect on the development of the bird.

7.5 Stress

Environmental stress can have a negative effect on daily weight gains. Any major stress that a chick undergoes can cause a limited period of slow or non-existent weight gain. It is not unusual for chicks that have been moved to another visual environment to experience a twenty-four hour period with little or no weight gain. This may occur even though digestion and crop motility remain the same. Apparently the stress involved in the move burns up the energy that would normally be used for growth. A similar experience may occur when a chick begins to grow its feathers. The first twenty-four hour period when feather development begins may be a day of no weight increase.

Chapter 8
Potential Health Problems in the Nursery

8.1 Aspiration

When a chick inhales formula or fluids it is said to have aspirated. Aspiration is usually due to some type of human error. The majority of aspirations commonly occur during the actual hand-feeding of the chick and can happen when using any type of feeding instrument. The accidental inhalation occurs when the chick stops swallowing, or refuses to swallow the formula, as it is placed into the mouth. At this moment the food begins to back up into the mouth and covers the entrance to the trachea. If the flow of formula is stopped immediately, aspiration can be prevented. It often occurs when the hand-feeder is not attentive enough to notice that the food has begun to back up into the mouth and does not terminate the flow. Formula served at the wrong temperature is a major cause of many chicks' refusal to swallow. Occasionally a chick may aspirate itself by putting pressure on its own crop and forcing the liquids into the mouth where they are inadvertently inhaled.

There are varying degrees of aspiration. In a situation where a chick inhales only a small quantity of formula the symptoms are similar to a child that has inhaled water in a swimming pool. Coughing, sneezing, skin color changes, a shaking of the head, and gasping for breath may occur. The chick usually recovers after the coughing stops. Any formula in the nostrils should be removed by sucking it up in a clean syringe. If the chick has failed to clear itself completely of all formula from the respiratory tract, a slight clicking or rasping sound may be heard during breathing. Anytime aspiration is suspected, antibiotic therapy should begin unless symptoms cease in a few hours.

In severe cases where the bird does not die immediately, the chick may be seen gasping for breath continually. The outlook for these chicks is poor. Occasionally oxygen and antibiotic therapy has been known to help. Immediate consultation with an avian veterinarian is recommended.

8.2 Aspergillosis

Aspergillis is a very common green-blue mold that grows on bread and other unrefrigerated food products. The mold produces spores that float through the air until they contact a surface that is conducive to their growth. These spores are always present in the air and are not problematic unless the immune system is compromised.

The dark, warm, and moist respiratory tract of a bird or even a human is the ideal place for optimum growth. Depending on the amount of spores contained in the air, the competent immune system can inhibit the growth of this mold. If the spore count is very high, even the best immune system may not be able to stop it. The bedding materials that are commonly used for baby parrots are an ideal growth medium for aspergillis spores. When this bedding becomes moist and soiled, the spores begin to grow and multiply. Keeping baby parrots on contaminated substrate is a perfect example of how this opportunistic spore can infect the chicks.

Symptoms of a problem may include some type of respiratory distress or a clicking noise while breathing. This clicking noise is the same as a chick that has inhaled small amounts of formula but if the noise is caused by food inhalation it will eventually subside, while babies infected with aspergillis will get sicker as time goes on. At this point, there is no completely effective treatment for aspergillosis. If babies are kept clean and healthy, the immune system can usually protect itself from infection. If infection has occurred and the chick is strong and healthy, the body may be able to fight the illness to a certain degree. In severe cases, the prospect of a long life is very grim.

8.3 Bacterial Infections

The most common cause of disease in the nursery is the invasion of harmful bacteria. Certain gram negative bacteria can cause crop stasis, stunting, malnutrition, or even death. Many times birds that show no outward signs of disease, yet are *poor-*

doers, may be suffering from a low grade bacterial infection. Even the cleanest of nurseries will eventually encounter bacterial problems.

If a bacterial infection is suspected, consultation with an avian veterinarian is necessary. A culture of the bacteria is taken from the site suspected of harboring the infection. If a respiratory infection is suspected and nasal discharge, excess mucous, or wheezing accompany the illness or if the bird shows no specific signs, the cloaca may be cultured since it is the site most likely to produce useful information. The culture is performed by inserting a cotton swab into the site selected. The swab is then placed in a sterile growth medium to keep the bacteria alive while it is being transported. Once in the lab, the bacteria is plated on agar plates where it can thrive and grow in large numbers. This facilitates identification of any bacteria that may be causing a problem. After the growth period, sensitivity to specific antibiotics can be tested. The results of the sensitivity testing allows your veterinarian to make a decision as to the drug of choice for treatment.

Since it usually takes several days to receive the culture results, it is a common practice to initiate treatment with some type of broad spectrum antibiotic after a gram's stain analysis shows a high gram negative bacterial count. This is done because while waiting for the results, the bacteria is multiplying in the laboratory and in the body of the chick. To allow a critically ill chick to die while waiting for lab results is unacceptable. Once your veterinarian receives the results he will either continue or change the antibiotic as determined by the sensitivity test.

Due to the rapidity in which a chick can succumb to an infection, many aviculturists begin what is known as a *shotgun* antibiotic treatment. This is most common when consultation with an avian veterinarian is not immediately possible. *Shotgun* treatment usually involves the use of a strong antibiotic that has, in the past, been effective against bacterial infections that they have encountered in other birds. Experience is mandatory in making the appropriate selections.

This type of treatment can cause problems. If the aviculturist makes a wrong guess, the use of a marginally effective or inappropriate antibiotic can prevent proper identification of the real problem. For this reason, whenever the decision to *shotgun* antibiotics is made, a cloacal swab or fecal sample should first be taken and refrigerated in case a professional evaluation is necessary at a later time.

Administration of inadequate dosages or inappropriate antibiotics can encourage resistant strains of bacteria. For this reason, *shotgun* treatments should be done only when absolutely necessary and when used by individuals experienced in antibiotic selection and dosing.

8.3.1 Secondary Infections

When a chick's immune system is compromised due to a viral, bacterial, or chlamydial (Psittacosis) problem, often an occult infection will surface. This infection is said to be secondary to the primary disease that caused the initial infection. Secondary infections can be caused by the overgrowth of a bacteria or fungi that previously existed in harmless quantities. This overgrowth is made possible by the destruction of normal competitive flora by the drug being used to treat the primary infection. If this previously harmless organism is not sensitive to the drug being used, a second antibiotic will have to be added to the primary treatment. This scenario most commonly takes place during treatment for psittacosis. *Tetracycline* and its derivatives, which are the drugs of choice when treating psittacosis, are often ineffective against many other pathogenic bacteria. With this in mind one must monitor the recovery of chicks closely. If a recovering chick takes a turn for the worst, a secondary infection should be suspected. Fungal infections are usually considered in this category. (See Fungal Infections)

8.4 Beak Injuries

Injuries involving the beak are usually inflicted by one nestmate to the other. It is quite common for two birds to lock beaks and pump vigorously to mimic the normal feeding response between parent and chick. This may result in punctures or breakage of the beak. Severe bacterial or fungal infections can develop in these areas if they are not treated. Antibiotic and anti-fungal ointments are available to be used in these cases.

Superficial wounds where no blood is present need only be kept clean of food and other foreign matter. Deep breaks or punctures may need to be treated and repaired by an avian specialist who has experience in beak repair. These deep wounds need to heal slowly in order to minimize scarring and deformations. A moisturizing type antibiotic ointment is used to slow the healing process and allow regrowth of the affected area. Some injuries may result in permanent deformities in spite of prompt attention.

When chicks continually inflict injury on each other, there is usually some type of nutritional or psychological imbalance. If the diet is balanced and all environmental factors are correct, chicks should not grab each other and pump so violently as to cause injury unless they are being underfed. These violent attempts to feed are caused by a lack of sufficient quantity, quality, or frequency of feedings.

8.5 Birth Defects

As the successful rearing of parrots in captivity increases, so will the number of unusual birth defects. At this point, the list is somewhat short but seems to be growing. The deadliest of these anomalies, where the entire spinal cord is exposed, is still extremely rare.

Rare birth defect where the yolk-sac forms around the body, preventing absorption and causing death.

Curved wing tip on left, normal wing on right. This is not a birth defect but caused by the wing tip being used by chick to keep balance against wall of brooding container. It can be reversed by taping wing into proper position.

8.5.1 Left Side Esophagus

Some chicks are hatched with their esophagus on the left side of their neck instead of the normal position on the right. This defect seems to be more prevalent in Macaws but has been noted in Amazons as well. The statistics for two of the largest producing farms in the United States show that in large birds this can occur as frequently as one in every three hundred hatchings. The left side opening does not interfere with the chick's normal feeding or ability to thrive. The hand-feeder must remember to feed these chicks with special attention in order to prevent a build-up of food in the mouth and possible aspiration. If unweaned, feeding should be demonstrated and if weaned, the condition should be shown to the new owners and veterinarian so that they will know that the bird swallows normally on the left side. If the bird should become ill and require force feeding, this information will be essential to avoid injury to the bird.

8.5.2 Curved Toes

Sometimes a chick will hatch with all of its toes curved inwards. This is easily noticeable by placing the chick on a flat

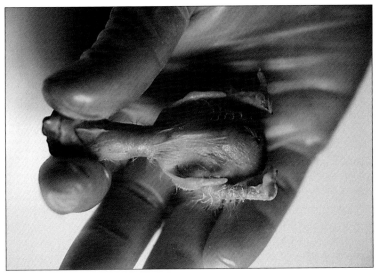

Amazon chick with left-side esophagus (filled with food) as well as a *missing crop*

surface. This condition varies in magnitude from a slight curving of the toes to a complete curving of the foot so that the chick appears to be walking on the sides of its feet. The authors have only seen this in small Conures and in Asian Parakeets.

It has been noted that in all birds with this problem, the eggs were incubated by the parents. Of further interest is the fact that the parents were new parents and had not raised young chicks for more than one or two seasons. After that time period, no more disfigured young were produced. The defect was not reproduced genetically when two affected siblings were inbred and probably occurs during the incubation period.

8.5.3 Distorted Head and Neck at Hatching

This is not a birth defect but a common and normal occurrence. The authors felt that this was the best category to describe this condition due to the number of phone calls received from new breeders claiming their chicks have a birth defect. Many times the chick will hatch with one side of its head completely indented and the opposite side grossly protruding. This can be accompanied by a misdirected beak as well as a swollen hatching or neck muscle. These abnormalities are caused by the cramped conditions inside of the egg. Worst cases are caused by high humidity during incubation, where moisture is retained in the egg and chick's body, leaving the chick with little room to move. It may take from a couple of hours to a few days for the shape of the head to return to normal.

8.5.4 Short Keel and Breast

On very rare occasions a chick will develop with an extremely short keel and breast muscle. Sometimes they are so short the heart will extend below them and appear to be directly below the skin. In these severe cases, the heart can be seen beating as the skin moves up and down with each beat. This condition is not necessarily fatal as long as injury does not occur to the chest area. Some aviculturists that have encountered this situation have called it *exposed heart*. Most of the cases that have occurred in domestic babies have ended in tragedy.

8.5.5 Missing Crop

On rare occasions a chick will hatch that has no crop. This situation is always fatal in the nest but hand-reared chicks can be saved if the esophagus empties into the digestive tract. These chicks must be fed every few hours as the esophagus will accommodate only a small amount of food. Care must be taken not to aspirate the chick by overfilling the neck area.

8.5.6 Missing Keel

Recently there have been a few cases where chicks have hatched with no breast or keel bone. These chicks appeared normal but had soft rounded abdomens. They did live to adulthood but their long term viability is still unknown. The breeding of birds with such anomalies is discouraged since the genetic foundation is unknown.

8.6 Bleeding (General)

Bleeding or bruising under the skin of young chicks is a possible indication of severe problems. Anytime chicks bleed or bruise for no obvious reason they should be immediately separated from the others and taken to a veterinarian. These chicks should be examined for indications that they may be suffering from viral pathogens.

8.6.1 Bleeding From Injury

Chicks that are injured by siblings or the nursery attendant can be treated at home in most cases. Broken blood feathers, injured beaks, or bites from other birds are the most common accidents that will be encountered. Control the bleeding by using pressure or a coagulating agent and gently clean the wounded area. A topical antibacterial cream or ointment may be sparingly applied. Injured blood feather shafts may need to be removed. If you have no experience at this, consult an avian veterinarian or experienced aviculturist for assistance.

8.6.2 Bleeding Umbilicus

Bleeding through the umbilicus is usually a problem associated with day-old incubator hatched chicks. Stop the bleeding by applying light pressure on the umbilical area. Use sterile gauze or tissue that is moistened with a 1% betadine solution. If this does not stop the bleeding in a short amount of time, try using *Quik Stop* or some other coagulating agent. After bleeding has been halted, gently clean the area with betadine solution.

In situations where the yolk sac or parts of the intestinal tract are protruding through the umbilicus, a veterinarian should be contacted immediately. Usually a suture or two will hold the umbilicus closed long enough for it to heal. Chicks with this problem may benefit from antibiotic therapy.

8.6.3 Bleeding Toes or Feet

Sometimes the substrate under a chick's feet will irritate the skin and cause bleeding. The irritation seems to worsen in a dry brooding situation. The use of rough paper towels with chicks that have very small feet and toes can create a severe bleeding problem. It can take as little as a few hours for small chicks to bleed to death if the situation is not brought under control.

Apply pressure using clean gauze or tissue. If the bleeding does not stop, try using some type of coagulating agent. To promote better healing, it is prudent to apply an antibacterial cream or ointment to the affected areas for a few days.

If blood loss was severe and the chick is pale or cool to the touch, it may need an injection of iron, fluid therapy or a transfusion. Keep these chicks warm and seek medical assistance. To avoid this situation, some aviculturists lubricate the feet of very small chicks with *KY Lubricating Jelly* or mild moisturizing creams made for human babies.

8.7 Broken Bones

The bones of baby birds are very soft and somewhat pliable. For this reason, broken bones are very rare in the nursery but when it occurs the major cause is nutritional deficiencies from improperly balanced formulas. Rickets or brittle bones in young chicks is an indication that a dietary evaluation is necessary.

Since baby birds grow very rapidly, bones heal at an astounding rate. The leg bones of very small chicks need only be properly placed and taped to a small splint. These bones may actually heal in as little as 72 hours but support should not be removed for at least seven to ten days. Bones left un-set may need to be re-broken and splinted for proper healing. In most cases, it is wise to consult with an avian veterinarian as early as possible for treatment and possible vitamin and mineral supplementation.

8.8 Burned Crops

The burning of the lining of the crop is caused by excessively hot food. Most crop burns are not apparent immediately but will slowly develop over a period of one or two days after the incident. The external color and texture of the crop changes to a rough yellowish-brown scar that develops from inside of the crop. This looks very similar to a black and blue bruise. The scar can become a scab and eventually rupture to the outside, causing formula to leak from the crop. In severe cases where the entire crop lining is affected, the chick will usually die before this happens. If the burn is slight or the scab develops and the chick lives, surgical removal of the scab and repair of the crop is possible.

Chicks that have ingested hot food will often exhibit erratic behavior when approached for feeding thereafter. They may roll over or resist food of any kind. When they are alone, they will often sit quietly with their eyes closed and their heads back. In minor cases there is often vomiting of formula or thick clear mucous after feeding.

An avian veterinarian or surgeon may be able to surgically remove the affected portion of the crop. This surgery cannot be performed until the burned areas have had time to show the effects of the damage. This waiting period will insure that all damaged tissue will be removed at one time so that there will be no need for a second surgery. Therapy after the surgery consists of antibiotics and smaller meals fed more often. Usually the crop will heal and slowly expand to accommodate larger quantities of food. The outlook for survival in many cases is good if the hand-feeder takes the time needed to keep the bird fed. Severely burned chicks whose entire crop is affected usually do not fair well and should be euthanized rather than slowly starved to death.

8.9 Clogged Cloaca

If the cloaca is masked over with dried feces, the chick cannot defecate and will eventually become very sick or die. Dried fecal matter can be easily removed by applying a piece of gauze moistened with warm water and slowly working the obstruction away.

Sometimes the cloaca becomes clogged from the inside. Fecal matter can often be seen through the skin on the chick's abdomen just above the opening of the vent. To open the cloaca, a very small cotton tipped swab is used. Moisten the swab in clean warm water or a sterile lubricating jelly and gently insert it into the cloaca. If the cloaca was clogged, fecal matter should follow the end of the swab as it is retracted.

It is important to monitor the defecation of young chicks. This is not always easy if the substrate used is wood shavings or corn cob bedding. Chicks are similar to human babies in this respect, they must eat and defecate regularly in order to grow. If either one fails to occur, the chick will weaken and eventually die. A lack of fecal matter in the brooder may be an indicator of future problems.

Severely burned crop showing formation of external scab at point of trauma

8.10 Clogged Nares (Nostrils)

Food often becomes dried and lodged in the nares of young chicks. In most cases, this is of no great consequence and given time, the blockage will usually clear itself.

If you desire to clean the nares of the chick yourself, it can be accomplished with a blunt object similar to the flat end of a toothpick. Gently clean the residue from the nares being cautious not to dig too deeply. On larger birds this may provoke a feeding response and cause a stabbing accident.

The nares can be flushed using warm sterile water or saline solution. This is usually done by gently instilling the liquid into the nares from a small syringe or eye dropper. This will often cause the chick to cough or sneeze but will have no ill effects if small quantities of liquid are used. One must take care not to aspirate the chick. The aviculturists may wish to perform this procedure themselves. If drugs or other additives are to be used, a veterinarian should be consulted.

8.11 Conjunctivitis

Conjunctivitis is almost as broad a term as *eye problem*. It usually refers to the inflamation of the conjunctival tissue surrounding the eye and underneath the eyelids. When this area is irritated it will swell, redden and sometimes cause tear production. The bird may squint the eye or hold it completely closed. The necessary course of action will be dependent upon the source of the irritation. If it is due to a harmless poke in the eye by a nest-mate, it will probably return to normal in about twenty-four hours. If there is no improvement, some type of bacterial infection should be suspected. The use of any broad spectrum ophthalmic antibiotic ointment or drops will usually solve the problem. In cases where an infection is not noticed until it is in the advanced stages, prolonged treatments may be necessary to effect a cure. Using these preparations at least three times a day will speed the healing process.

Inflamation that does not respond to normal antibiotic therapy could be caused by a viral or fungal agent. If mycoplasma or chlamydia is the culprit, you may have to design an ophthalmic treatment regime that includes drugs specifically designed to fight these agents. *Tetracycline* ophthalmic ointments have been used effectively in the past.

If the irritation is being caused by a fungus, the choice is usually oral treatment with *Ketoconazol* although there are some new antifungal ophthalmic agents on the market that show great promise. If these new products are not obtainable, *Ketaconazole* will fight the infection systemically.

Viral eye problems must run their course. There is little that can be done to cure the problem but supportive therapy will help to keep the chick more comfortable. The use of ophthalmic drops and ointments will help to fight off any possible bacterial problem that may occur as a secondary infection. In the past, these viral eye problems such as poxvirus, were only seen in newly imported baby parrots. This is no longer true and unfortunately they have surfaced in domestically produced young also. The cause of the problem must be determined by an avian veterinarian and an effective treatment regime prescribed.

In situations where the eyelid has become pasted shut, the eye must be opened by using warm compresses to loosen the dried exudate so the eyelids can be gently forced apart. This must be performed before every treatment where the eye is sealed shut. If the eye is allowed to remain closed and a serious infection results, blindness may occur.

The recovery of eye problems during treatment is usually very rapid. Sometimes there is a small, hard, lump of exudate (often it is pus) lodged between the layers of the conjunctiva. If a lump is noticed, the chick should be taken to a veterinarian to have the lump removed. In most cases it can be pushed out with skillful fingertip manipulation. Once this is removed, recovery should be rapid.

If recovery of any eye problem is slow, a vitamin A deficiency should be suspected. Supplementation of vitamin A will usually lead to recovery.

8.12   Constricted Toe Syndrome

The cause of this syndrome is still unknown. In old literature it is said to be caused by a bacterial infection. Recent observations claim that it may be due to low humidity brooding. The problem first appears as a malformed toe that looks as if a string had been tied around it very tightly. Circulation to the tip of the toe is limited or in severe cases, completely stopped. Massage therapy can be helpful in some cases. If there is no response,

Typical lesion associated with constricted toe syndrome

amputation is often necessary. Some suggest making a small incision at the constriction point. This may prevent formation of scar tissue and eliminate the need for amputation.

8.13 Constipation

Although true constipation is rare it can be caused by severe dehydration. In this case, what little droppings there are will be very hard and dry compared to normal feces. Treatment for dehydration and the administration of a few drops of mineral oil into the cloaca may help to relieve this problem. In most cases, however, lack of defecation is not caused by simple constipation but is a sign of other problems. The cloaca can become clogged from dried feces or can be plugged from the inside. Relief for this situation is imperative or the chick may die. A small cotton-tipped swab should be moistened with mineral oil and carefully inserted into the cloaca. If the obstruction is in the area of the vent, feces should follow the withdrawal of the swab. If this procedure does not solve the problem, a blockage may exist higher up in the digestive tract. An avian veterinarian should be consulted at once.

8.14 Crooked or Abnormal Beak Growth

When hand rearing chicks of the larger species (i.e. Macaws, Cockatoos, or Amazons) crooked or twisted beaks may be noticed. Many theories have evolved as to the causes of these anomalies. It has been suggested that many are caused by improper handling when feeding. This suppositon is supported by the fact that most are twisted from left to right. This is the way the upper mandible is pushed when the chick is fed properly. They can also be caused by the use of round brooding containers, malnutrition, certain isolated infections or possibly even genetics. Many speculate that damage to the cells near the base and the tip contribute to misdirected growth. This may also occur during incubation.

8.15 Crop Stasis

Crop stasis refers to a condition in which the food does not move out of the crop and into the digestive tract. It is rarely caused by a primary crop disorder. Whenever crop stasis occurs it requires immediate attention. In fact, one should not wait for actual stoppage to occur before attention is given to alleviating the cause of the problem. There is usually a period of extreme slowing prior to actual stasis. If proper care is given at this time, a more rapid and less stressful recovery is possible.

Early symptoms of beak misalignment

There are several things which may lead to this condition, not all of which are disease related. Improper brooding, improper feeding, obstruction in the crop, fungal and or bacterial infection, or the invasion of some viruses can all be responsible for crop stasis. Whenever drastic slow down occurs, it should never be ignored. Failure to recognize this warning sign can be fatal to the bird.

8.15.1 Improper Feeding

Feeding food that is too thick for young chicks to digest will cause crop stasis immediately. In day-old chicks, this condition may be irreversible and may cause severe dehydration that could claim the life of the chick. The only possibility there is to reverse the condition is to feed very warm water with extreme caution, this can be augmented with subcutaneous fluids. The warm water will re-hydrate the food so it can be passed. In many cases however, the dehydration that has already occurred while the system tried to digest the thick (dry) food, brings the chick to a critical state from which there is no return.

In older chicks, where the condition is treated in a timely manner, it is usually reversible. Warm water must be added carefully to the crop by using a catheter or gavage needle. Gently massage the crop to mix the water with the hardened contents. The re-hydrated food should, at this point, pass into the digestive tract. In cases where this does not work, the crop will need to be emptied (see How to Empty the crop, section **10.3**). Sometimes the body will extract liquids from the crop contents causing a repeat of the problem. In this case, the crop must be emptied again and the chick should be fed fluids. Liquid feedings should be fed several times. When it appears that digestion has returned to normal, food can be thickened slowly, with each feeding, until proper consistency is attained.

Food that is fed too cold can also lead to this condition. A large quantity of very cold food fed to a young chick, can drain the chick's body heat and stop the digestive system from functioning normally. This situation usually occurs by accident. The food must first be removed from the crop, then warm food should be fed (if accepted), and brooding temperature should be increased. If the chick will not accept food, do not force it, but wait until the body temperature is back to normal and try again. Many times a chick that is too cold will not accept food.

Hot food can cause crop damage. If the damage is in the area of the entrance to the digestive system, crop stasis will usually result. In cases such as this, surgery by an avian veterinarian is necessary if the bird is to live.

Sour food is a major cause of crop stasis. This is the condition that is commonly called *Sour Crop* or *acidosis*. The more sour the food, the slower it passes. The slower it passes, the more sour it gets. This snowballing process can eventually lead to the complete shut-down of the digestive system due to the acidic nature of soured food. Although this condition can be brought about by the use of food that has already soured before it is fed, this is not usually the case. It often begins with the continual addition of food to a crop that has not been given a chance to empty.

Sour food that remains in the crop from the previous feeding will cause fresh food to sour at an accelerated rate. If digestion is proceeding at a normal rate, this is allowable as long as the crop completely empties at least once in a given twenty-four hour period. Those that insist on the crop being empty at every feeding can wind up with chicks that exhibit slow growth or are stunted. Most aviculturists choose the early morning feeding time as their *crop empty* time. In cases where a twenty-four hour period has passed and the chick has not been given the opportunity to empty, you must wait a few hours to let the old food digest. If the crop does not empty in a reasonable amount of time it must be emptied by the aviculturist.

If this protocol is not followed and the crop is not given a chance to empty every day, the eventual result can be total crop stasis. In this situation, waiting for the crop to empty is futile and the chick will starve to death with a full crop of food. If complete stasis occurs, the crop must be emptied to eliminate the sour food. Fill the crop with warm water and empty it again. Repeat this *washing* procedure several times until the water removed is clear. Some aviculturists prefer to use a mild *Nolvasan* solution or baking soda preparation as the final rinse to change the ph of the crop. Anytime crop stasis occurs, dehydration may follow, therefore subcutaneous fluids are usually indicated along with injectable antibiotics.

Although the consulting veterinarians for this book stated that the following procedure is not *common practice* we have had the experience that suggests in cases of simple sour crop where no bacteria problem is suspected, once the wash is completed, fill the crop with thin formula making sure to feed the normal quantity. We believe that filling the crop completely will increase the downward pressure and help the food to begin to pass in a more timely manner. Once total crop stasis or extreme slow down has occurred due to sour crop, the crop will have to be emptied between every feeding until the digestion resumes its normal time interval. This means if a chick is being fed three times a day, the crop may have to be emptied and washed of old food at all three feedings. Do not make the mistake, as many have, of believing that feeding small quantities will eliminate the necessity of emptying the crop between feedings. When stasis has occurred from sour crop, the downward pressure from the full crop is necessary to alleviate the problem in a timely manner.

8.15.2 Improper Brooding

Crop stasis can be caused by brooder temperatures that are too low or too high. In very young chicks, too low a brooder temperature will cause digestion to stop. In older chicks, too high a temperature will have the same effect. This problem can be alleviated by readjusting brooding temperatures to the proper level. Once the chick warms or cools in the correct temperature, digestion usually resumes at a normal rate. (Consult sections **2.7, 2.7.1, 2.7.2, 2.7.3**, Brooding)

8.15.3 Illness

Bacterial or viral illness can cause an immediate slowing of crop motility and is the most common cause of crop stasis. In cases of viral infection, many times the chick dies before anything can be done. Sudden death of any chick warrants a professional necropsy to determine causal factors. Bacterial infections affect digestion to varying degrees. If the crop is moving slowly, there is still time to administer an oral antibiotic. When movement of food has completely stopped oral antibiotics are useless as they will only sit in the crop. In cases such as this, bacterial cultures and injectable antibiotics will be necessary as well, subcutaneous fluids are strongly recommended.

Many times a chick that is not digesting normal formula due to a bacterial infection, will digest fluids with greater ease. It is common practice to combine some form of concentrated high

Soured food or a high bacteria count in the crop has been known to cause the production of gas.

caloric supplement that does not contain fat with a hydrating liquid such as *Pedialyte, Ricelyte,* or lactated ringers. This mixture is fed in place of formula as it will pass quicker and provide needed energy and hydration to the recovering chick. As the chick's digestion returns to normal, feed thinned formula and slowly thicken to normal consistency.

Fungal infections in the digestive tract can also cause crop stasis. A total stoppage of the crop does not usually occur until the infection is severe. In many advanced cases, regurgitation is common. When this happens, filling the crop half-full with *Nystatin* diluted with warm water will often stop the regurgitation. Further treatments with some type of anti-fungal drug is necessary.

8.16 Cuts or Lacerations of the Skin

Some baby parrots have a knack for injuring themselves. Quite often they injure each other in an attempt to feed. Depending on the severity of the problem, a mild antibacterial ointment can be applied sparingly and is usually available from your veterinarian. If your local drug store sells antibacterial ointments made for babies, these can be used as well.

Bandaging cuts usually proves futile as the birds will almost always remove them but it should still be attempted. Keep all cuts clean and treat them often with the antibacterial ointments; the wounds should heal with no problems. Deep lacerations will need to be sutured by an avian practitioner.

8.17 Dark Areas at the Base of the Skull

On the lower rear section of the chick's head, a dark red, purple, or black and blue mark may appear. This occurs during severe dehydration, stunting, difficult hatching, and some viral infections. Isolation of the chick is suggested until the cause can be determined by the avian veterinarian.

8.18 Dehydration

Tissue dehydration in young chicks is usually secondary to bacterial infections or some other illness. During crop stasis, chicks will dehydrate as the body utilizes the moisture from the

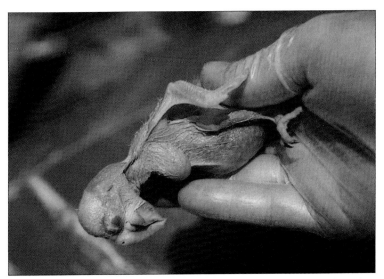

Stunted ten-day-old macaw chick exhibiting signs of severe dehydration and malnutrition.

tissues. Symptoms in a naked chick include a darkening of the skin, from a healthy pink, to an almost red, appearance. They often have a slightly boney look. When the skin is pinched it will return to its normal position very slowly. Replenishment of moisture is imperative. If the crop is still motile, feeding formula with plenty of extra water or *Ricelyte* mixed in may solve the problem. If the crop has slowed substantially or stopped, subcutaneous injections of lactated ringers solution is helpful. In advanced and severe cases, the only hope may be for intravenous injection of fluids. Aviculturists with no experience at this procedure should contact an avian veterinarian for assistance.

8.19 Diarrhea

This condition can be very difficult to diagnose and must be distinguished from polyuria in hand-feeding chicks. The feces of most chicks still being fed some type of feeding formula are often loose and may even be slightly watery. The consistency of the feces will depend on the contents of the hand-feeding formula. If the feces are always very watery, it may be wise to consult a veterinarian.

True diarrhea is actually very rare. When diagnosed, it must be treated as dictated by the results of diagnostic tests. The underlying problem must be identified and resolved. If the stools are loose simply due to the nature of the diet, *Kaopectate* may be used to help eliminate the problem. If fruit additives are being used, they can be reduced or eliminated until the condition is under control.

8.20 Dry Skin

Flakey dry skin is, in most cases, caused by dry brooding. The addition of water to the brooding environment will usually solve the problem. Dry skin is most often noticed when only one or two chicks are being brooded in each brooder unit. When three or more chicks are in the same brooder, the moisture produced by their transpiration and droppings is usually sufficient to keep skin hydrated. Very dry brooding conditions can be dangerous to chicks with tiny delicate toes or wing tips. These extremities can dry and crack causing sufficient bleeding to weaken or even kill the chick.

8.21 Feces: What is Normal?

It would be impossible to describe all colors, consistencies and quantities of normal feces. All of these factors are influenced by the type of formula that is being used as well as the condition of the chick. It can be stated that fresh feces should not have a foul odor. Anytime a strong odor is noticed in feces of young chicks, it is an indication of a digestive problem or bacteria or fungal infection.

The feces of young chicks are usually different than that of adult birds. Most are not as well formed and are variable in color and consistency. Droppings consist of three separate parts. Normal droppings are made up of varying quantities of fecal matter, white urates, and clear liquid. All of these must be considered separately in monitoring the condition of a chick by *reading* the droppings.

Fecal matter is the remains of the digested food. In a healthy chick, the color of this matter can be any shade of yellow, brown, or green, depending on the formula that is being fed. Immediately after hatch, if the chick has any retained yolk to be digested, the fecal matter created by the digestion of the yolk will be a tar-like translucent green. As the yolk is totally utilized, the feces will change to a more normal color and consistency. Red or black feces are indicative of a major problem and veterinary consultation should be sought immediately. There are rare instances where reddish discoloration may be caused by droppings interacting with the substrate material.

The normal consistency of feces can range from that of prepared oatmeal to a firmer more defined mass like that of an adult bird. When the consistency of the fecal matter is so fluid that it ceases to hold any form after excretion, it is considered diarrhea and is usually due to bacterial or fungal problems. Fecal matter that is too dry and hard (like putty) is indicative of dehydration and it must be determined whether this is caused by a lack of water in the formula or because of a physical problem. If adding more water to the formula does not create a more hydrated stool a veterinarian should be consulted.

The white portion of the droppings, commonly called the urates, should be pure white. Whenever the color changes to any shade of yellow, the bird is usually in trouble as this can be indicative of a liver or kidney problem. If this problem persists for more than twelve hours, veterinary consultation is warranted. The quantity of white urates varies from one dropping to the other. In fact, it is normal to have an occasional dropping that contains no white matter. Continued absence of the white urates in the droppings may be caused by a digestive disorder.

The third part of a normal dropping is the clear liquid. Although any large quantities of clear fluid that is excreted with a dropping is unusual in adult birds, it is common and not necessarily a problem in chicks still being hand fed with formula. If it begins to appear in large quantities, it could be a sign of severe problems such as kidney disease, especially if the presence of white urates is decreased in the same dropping. This situation will often be noticed during antibiotic therapy where a drug that is toxic or damaging to the kidneys is being used. Notify the supervising veterinarian if these symptoms are noticed as they may want to change therapy if long term treatment is planned.

8.22 Fungal Problems (General)

Fungal problems are usually, but not always, a secondary infection associated with a depressed immune system. They will often appear in conjunction with or immediately following a bacterial infection, antibiotic therapy, or viral attack.

8.22.1 Recognition of the Problem

Fungal colonies in the crop may be noticeable as small white specks on the inside of the translucent skin of the crop. As they grow they may coat the entire inside of the crop and cause considerable crop slowing or total stasis. Once into the digestive tract, malnutrition occurs from the hampered absorption of nutrients in the formula.

If the fungus is detected early, it may only be in the mouth of the bird. At this stage it is very easy to see and looks like very small white spots. In many cases it may present itself as a diffuse whitish area in the mouth or on the tongue. Any time a portion of the black skin in the mouth changes from deep black to greyish, a problem is usually brewing. Treatment is warranted before it spreads through the entire digestive system or worse, the entire body. Oral anti-fungal medications such as *Nystatin, Ketaconozole,* or *Nolvasan* solutions can be used. In most infections that only involve the mouth or choanal slit, washing the mouth with *Nolvasan* solution a couple of times a day for a week will solve the problem. In cases where the infection has entered the crop or digestive tract, *Nystatin* or *Ketaconozole* will need to be administered and consultation with a veterinarian will be necessary.

8.22.2 During Antibiotic Treatments

When a chick is being treated with antibiotics, the immune system is generally compromised enough to allow the growth of opportunistic fungal spores within the chick's body. For this reason many avian veterinarians will treat chicks with an oral anti-fungal in conjunction with the antibiotic therapy. Usually anti-fungals are continued for three to five days after termination of antibiotic treatments. This is because antibiotic therapy destroys beneficial competitive bacteria which allows candidel overgrowth.

8.22.3 In Wet or Humid Climates

Fungal problems seem to be more common in hot, humid climates. These conditions are ideal for spore growth and an infestation can progress rapidly throughout the nursery. Periodic visual inspections and cultures are warranted when raising chicks in a moist environment. Preventative treatment programs may be helpful and should be prescribed by an avian veterinarian.

8.22.4 In Food Sources

Grain type foods, dry biscuits, or products that are made with yeast may be harboring the spores of dangerous fungi. This is the reason why most foods should be cooked thoroughly before being fed to young chicks. Pre-manufactured mixes that are intended to be used with the addition of warm water often will lose their nutritional value if cooked. These formulas should be discarded if not used immediately.

8.22.5 In the Mouth and Beaks of Large Birds

On rare occasions, when hand-feeding large birds such as Macaws, large Cockatoos, or Amazons, formula may become lodged in certain areas of the mouth or beak. If this food is allowed to remain, it can become tainted with bacteria or fungi. In individuals that have a propensity for this problem, a cotton swab moistened with *Nolvasan* solution (20cc/cup water) should be wiped under the tongue and in any area where food may become trapped. If this procedure is followed several times a week, fungal growth will not be a problem.

8.22.6 Treatments

Treatment of a systemic fungal infection is usually accomplished with one of today's anti-fungal drugs. In aviculture the most commonly used drugs are *Nystatin, Ketaconozole,* or *Nolvasan* solution (unscented). Anti-fungal medicines are usually administered orally, topically, or by nebulization so as to make direct contact with the fungal growth. The type of medication used will depend on the location and severity of infection, the species of fungi, and age of the chick to be treated. The avian veterinarian will prescribe the best medication for the problem.

When infection is confined to the mouth and inside of the beak, the fungus can be swabbed with any of the anti-fungals mentioned. This procedure needs to be accomplished twice a day for a minimum of seven days. Another precaution that needs to be addressed is the fact that anti-fungal medications become less effective when saturated with organic material. This means that adding them to the formula is much less effective than administering them on an empty crop. Since most of them have a bitter taste, this is not always easy. Care must be taken not to aspirate the chick when feeding it the medication.

8.22.7 Preventatives

Preventing yeast or fungal infections is usually a question of good hygiene and careful formula preparation. Some aviculturists use powdered or liquid *Nystatin* stirred directly into the hand-feeding formula. This of course, is meant to serve as a preventative to fungal growth. The biggest problem with this is that the organic composition of the formula will weaken the effect of the medication. If a problem does develop, a much stronger anti-fungal may need to be used to kill the fungi.

Swabbing the mouths of chicks with a mixture of *Nolvasan* solution and water can also be helpful in moist climates or where contaminated food is suspected. The strength of the solution depends on the severity of the problem. A weak solution would be one of twenty milliliters of *Nolvasan* to one gallon of water. Stronger mixtures of up to fifty percent *Nolvasan* have been used. Strong solutions are used as a topical cure only, they are not to be fed to the chick as a systemic medication. Weaker solutions are safe to use as drinking water for weaning chicks in order to control minor fungal problems.

8.22.8 Candida

Candida albicans is the most common type of fungal growth found in young psittacines. The spores of this fungi are present in the environment and are opportunistic in nature. The first signs of infection are usually small mucoid white spots inside the beak or mouth of the chick. If unnoticed and untreated, candida will continue to grow and multiply within the body of the chick. The presence of candida can also cause crop slowing, total crop stasis, malnutrition, incessant begging for food, stunting, lethargy or even death.

8.23 Lethargy

Lethargy (extreme laziness) and lack of movement can be an indication of illness. Baby parrots are not very active when young, but activities increase as the chicks mature. If the feeding response is weak or absent and the chick is very lethargic, lacking response to the touch, check environmental factors (brooder temperatures) for possible causes. Cold brooding is a main cause of lethargy. If temperatures are correct, gram stains or cultures for possible bacterial or fungal infections may be warranted.

8.24 Malnutrition

Malnutrition can be caused by any number of things from bad feeding formulas to insufficient food intake. Most monkey biscuit based formulas as well as some of the prepared formulas provide many of the needed nutrients for normal growth. The method of preparation, storage, and the feeding management program greatly influence whether or not the bird will receive these required vitamins and minerals.

8.24.1 Signs of Malnutrition

Signs of malnutrition are as varied as the reasons they occur. Some examples are: the chick appears boney and thin; has dull (not bright) eyes; is very small for its age; feathers late; opens its eyes very high on the eyelid instead of in the middle, or produces feathers that are margined with black, an unusual color; misdirected growth.

8.24.2 Causes of Malnutrition

Probably the major cause of malnutrition in the nursery is inexperience at hand-rearing. If a person does not know what a chick is supposed to look like at a certain age, they have no mode of reference. Inexperienced hand-feeders may not feed often enough, provide sufficient volume, adjust brooders properly, use supplements correctly, or even feed a nutritious diet.

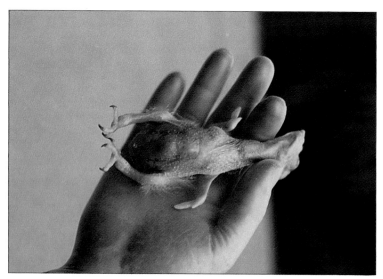

Amazon chick exhibiting deformed legs caused by calcium absorption problems. The hemorrhages (dark red spots) that appear on the breast, although caused in this case by malabsorption of other nutrients, are similar to those that may appear with papova virus.

Aside from inexperience, chicks may suffer from malnutrition if they have absorption problems and cannot utilize the nutrients in the formula. Certain species have a propensity for specific absorption problems (e.g. African Greys have calcium absorption problems). It is important to know as much as possible about the species that is being hand-reared so the feeder knows the signs to look for.

Bacterial or fungal infections may lead to malnutrition. In cases of malabsorption or indigestion, where the crop slows or stops completely, the nutrients in the formula remain in the crop or are not absorbed from the digestive tract. The longer the time period of abnormal digestion, the more severe will be the malnutrition that is caused.

8.24.3 Stunting

Stunting syndrome is caused by malnutrition. The severity of the case will depend on how long the bird was undernourished and to what extent. It is also believed that if a chick is brooded too long at a high temperature, stunting will result. Signs of this syndrome can be any or all of the list below.

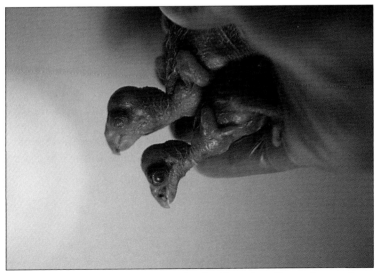

Amazon chicks of the same age demonstrating the effects of stunting syndrome on lower chick.

- Thin boney appearance
- Large disproportionate head for the body
- Misshapen head where a noticeable dip occurs directly behind the nares at the joining of the upper beak to the skull
- Enlarged posterior of the skull
- Long thin legs and wings
- Weight is considerably below normal
- Late feathering
- Crooked or malformed feathers
- Slow crop
- Recurring bacterial or fungal infections

In some cases the addition of digestive enzymes to the formula can help a bird with its growth. In nurseries where many birds are stunted, a thorough evaluation of diet and feeding procedures is in order.

8.25 Nasal Discharge

Discharge from the nares is usually caused by irritation of the sinuses. Sometimes the cause can be as simple as a dusty substrate where the dust irritates the sinuses. Rarely, there are cases where a chick is hatched with sinus problems that will continue throughout its life. In all other cases, it is usually due to an infectious agent.

This agent can be confined to the sinuses. Many times the use of ophthalmic antibiotic preparations placed directly into the nares can cure the problem. In more serious infections, the bird may need to be treated systemically with oral or injectable antibiotics.

If antibiotic nose drops are prescribed by your veterinarian, you must be sure to clean the nares of mucous prior to treatment. This is done by placing the tip of a clean syringe directly over the nostril opening and gently withdrawing the mucous into the syringe.

8.26 Pendulous (Stretched) Crop

The crop can be stretched beyond its elastic capability. Once stretched, crop stasis, sour crop and other digestive disorders may occur. When the crop is stretched so that it hangs down overlapping the keel, sour crop can occur from the food that is always present.

If overstretching occurs, there are ways to help the crop empty. One method is to put a support around the bottom of the crop to lift it into normal position. This helps the food enter the digestive tract rather than remain in the folded flap of extra crop tissue. An old tube sock or tape that sticks to itself (*Micropore, Vetwrap*) can be cut to the appropriate size and positioned where it is lifting the crop into place. Surgery is also an option. An avian surgeon can remove a portion of the crop and alleviate the emptying problem.

Care should be taken not to overstretch the crop of any bird. If the crop begins to hang when the bird is standing upright, the amount of food fed may need to be reduced before the situation becomes permanent. Large macaws and stunted birds seem to be more prone to the problem.

8.27 Periodic Gasping

When small amounts of food are aspirated into the chick's lungs, the chick will often gasp for air. The aspiration may occur from improper feeding or the chick may aspirate itself by leaning on a full crop and forcing the food up into the mouth. Anytime a baby appears to be gasping for breath, it is in urgent need of medical attention.

Antibiotics, heat and oxygen may help to alleviate the problem. Care must be taken to avoid repeated aspiration or death may ensue.

8.28 Psittacosis

Psittacosis is the disease that is commonly known as parrot fever. If allowed to enter the nursery, it can spread very quickly and infect birds that may not show symptoms until stressed. The most common symptoms are the continued loss of weight with no hampered digestion, green urates, and overall lethargy in advanced cases. Treatment consists of the use of *Tetracycline* or *Tetracycline* derivatives. Your veterinarian should make the decision as to the drug of choice in each case.

Efforts are made to eliminate psittacosis by treating all parent stock in the aviaries simultaneously to purge them of the disease.

New additions to the breeding flock should also be treated whether or not they show symptoms. This is to ensure that reinfection of the flock does not occur.

8.29 Punctured Crops

Punctures in the crop are the biggest problem associated with tube or gavage feeding. Avoiding the problem through careful administration of food is much easier than treatment of affected chicks. The outlook is grim for a chick that has had several milliliters of formula pass through the wall of the crop and collect underneath the skin of the body cavity.

A sure sign that a puncture has occurred is the absence of the food in the crop after feeding. This is a serious situation. In cases where the puncture is slight, small amounts of food will leak from the hole and cause an infection and inflammation of the surrounding tissue. Fluids (edema) will usually fill the surrounding area and the bird will die without medical attention. Crop surgery and antibiotic therapy may be the only hope for the chick's survival.

8.30 Punctured Esophagus

When the tip of a syringe, feeding tube, or gavage is accidentally forced through the esophagus wall, veterinary assistance is necessary immediately. It is not always obvious that a puncture has occurred, and depending on its location, it may be impossible to determine at the time of occurrence. In cases where the puncture is high in the esophagus, local swelling may occur on the side of the neck or under the lower mandible of the beak. These swellings are usually of a translucent pink color due to the build-up of edema where the food is irritating the surrounding tissue. An avian veterinarian may be able to flush the food from the affected area and administer an antibiotic to curtail further infection. If left untreated, chicks usually die in two to four days from infection.

Subsequent feedings may need to be accomplished using a feeding tube or gavage. This will ensure that the food enters the crop and does not continually irritate affected areas.

8.31 Skin Color Changes

When a chick is suffering from some disorder, it is usually reflected in the color of the skin. Technically, the color change occurs in the musculature below the skin as the skin itself is very transparent.

Dark red color is usually an indication of rapid dehydration caused by a bacterial infection. Fluid therapy is the first step to helping the chick. If the crop is still emptying in a timely manner, extra fluids can be fed orally to help re-hydrate the chick. If the chick is not passing fluids orally, subcutaneous fluids will be necessary. Bacterial tests should be performed and analyzed to identify the problem.

Chicks that appear very pale, almost white, can be suffering from a virus, egg yolk poisoning, or are losing blood. If no bleeding is apparent externally, the problem may be internal. The body extremities may also feel cool to the touch even if kept in a warm brooder. In these cases medical assistance is suggested immediately. Vitamins K, B, and iron supplementation is advised if the bird is hemmorrhaging.

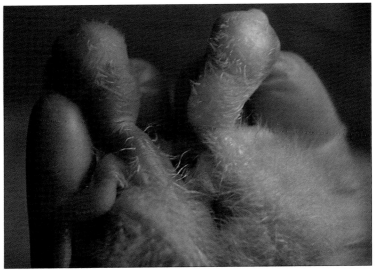

Typical paling associated with yolk-sac poisoning as well as other illnesses. Normal coloration shown by chick on right.

8.32 Skin Temperature Changes

During illness, the temperature of a naked chick's body often feels cool to the touch. This is not a good sign and usually the situation ends in disaster.

Place chicks in a very warm brooder (92-97°F) immediately. If digestion is good, feed the chick its normal formula mixed approximately half and half with water or lactated ringers solution. Be sure to heat formula to a high, but safe temperature (108°F) before feeding. Cool formula will lower the body temperature even further.

High calorie food supplements such as *Instant Ounces* can be added to the thinned formula to help increase energy levels and, hopefully, body temperature.

Medical therapy is usually useless in this case but may be helpful in certain circumstances. Therapy often consists of steroids, fluids, and antibiotic treatments as well as heat and oxygen administration.

8.33 Sour Crop

The term *sour crop* is an old term used to describe a condition where the food does not move out of the crop with sufficient rapidity to keep it from turning sour. This souring effect will cause crop slowdown. If allowed to continue, crop stasis will occur. This was a major problem in the past when it was not realized how important disinfection of formula was. Crop stasis (stoppage) caused by feeding sour food is becoming more of a rarity. This subject in its entirety is discussed in section 8.15 of this chapter. Bear in mind that not only can crop stasis be the cause of sour crop, but that sour crop can be the cause of crop stasis.

8.34 Splayed Legs

Splayed legs is a condition in which one or both of the chick's legs extend outwardly from the hip instead of downward under the chick to support its weight. Frequently, this condition is caused by improper nutrition or bedding that does not give proper footing to the chick. In rare cases, splaying has been thought to be caused by hatch-related problems or disease.

Improper nutrition may be caused not only by a poorly balanced diet, but also by absorption problems in specific birds. These absorption problems can be caused by disease or genetics. Many times these problems can be corrected by supplementing the chick with calcium and vitamins along with taping the legs into the correct position for a few days. The legs of the chick should be brought into the normal position and taped with medical tape or *Vetwrap*. This is easier done by taping the legs together above the ankles and allowing enough space between them so they grow naturally. It is often necessary to place the chick in a tight, padded container or cup to limit the ability of the legs to push out to the side. Since growth is at a rapid rate, it may take as little as three or four days to correct the problem. Even though the legs may be mended in a few days, the tape and movement restriction should continue for at least one week. In some cases it is not necessary to tape the legs, restricting the chick's movement by placing it in the tight container will correct the deformity.

Splayed legs can occur when a chick is kept on a surface that is slippery and allows the legs to slide apart. Many aviculturists keep brooding chicks in plastic bins. These bins have smooth surfaces on the bottom. The nesting material added (substrate) must be deep enough to keep the chick's feet from penetrating the substrate and slipping on the smooth surface of the bin bottom. Paper towels, when used as substrate, usually do not cause a slipping problem. A small percentage of chicks, however, do need the extra support that a deep bedding offers. When problems are noticed one might try a bed of deep wood shavings or some other type of bedding.

8.35 Stunted Growth Versus Stunting Syndrome

Stunted growth and stunting syndrome are not necessarily the same problem. With stunting syndrome there is almost always some degree of permanent physical deformity. Stunted growth however, can be merely a case of slower growth. Many times a chick that receives proper nutrition and has no absorption problems, but is not fed often enough, will grow at a much slower rate than a similar chick that is fed more frequently or in greater quantities. To a minor degree this capacity to grow at a slower rate, can be noticed in most clutches of parent raised birds. A clutch of three chicks that hatch at approximately two to three days apart can become separated in development by as much as a week or more. The reason is that the oldest, strongest chick demands more food so the parent has less to give to the younger siblings. For this reason it is not uncommon for chicks that are only three days apart to appear to be ten days apart in the latter stages of development. This is a natural phenomenon that does not result in any malformation to the smaller chick although it might result in the bird not reaching its maximum size potential.

Stunting syndrome, on the other hand, occurs after a chick's growth pattern has already been set at an accelerated rate. A sudden lack of nutrition due to disease or inadequate hand feeding does not initially slow down development. The chick continues to develop at the accelerated rate without the proper building blocks. This is the reason deformities occur. The growth pattern of a chick (from observation in the nursery) seems to be set in the first few days of life. Once you have established a rapid growth pattern, then feeding must continue at that intensity or the chick will begin to stunt. If after the rapid pattern is set, the quantity or frequency of feeding is diminished drastically, then stunting syndrome is likely to occur. In other words, if the hand feeder pushes a young chick to grow and gain weight then suddenly becomes inattentive about feeding, the chick could go into stunting syndrome. In cases where the hand feeder is somewhat lazy from the beginning, the chick will usually become a slow grower but not necessarily enter into stunting syndrome. Cases of stunting syndrome have been noticed where chicks have been brooded too long at high temperatures. If not corrected, continued elevated temperature causes digestion to slow which then slows nutrition and the chick may develop the syndrome. The symptoms and physical anomalies of the syndrome are listed under the malnutrition section of this book.

8.36 Subcutaneous Emphysema

Subcutaneous emphysema occurs when air leaks out of a bird's internal air sacs and is trapped between the skin and the muscle tissue. In serious cases, the entire body of the bird can be affected. This gives the bird a *puffy* look as the air dissects between the layers of skin. In less serious cases the affected areas may be confined to a small spot or section of skin. Personal experience with this problem has shown it can be caused in two ways.

Injury to one of a bird's air sacs is the least common cause of this condition. Air sacs can be injured or ruptured through mishandling, rough play, or long-term bacterial infections. The most common cause of the condition is a complication of a surgical sexing method called endoscopy. During the examination, the veterinarian will put a tiny hole in the chick's side near the lower air sac. The instrument is inserted through the skin, muscular wall, and the air sac to view the sexual organs. This procedure can be performed at a very young age in order to determine which birds to hold back as future breeders. The problem occurs when the hole in the skin heals before the hole in the muscle wall. This allows air to pass from the air sac through the muscle wall where it is then trapped under the skin.

Treatment of this condition is similar to that of popping a balloon full of air. Feathers should be separated in the area with the greatest inflation, where the skin does not contain numerous blood vessels. A sharp sterile object can be used to make a small tear in the skin. The air is then squeezed out of this incision. In cases where this is a complication of surgical sexing and if the hole in the muscular wall has healed, the remedy will be permanent. Where this is due to a rupture from an injury, the procedure may have to be performed several times as the bird will re-inflate in a few days due to the slow healing of the muscle layers. In some cases, where this rupture is caused by injury, the problem may reoccur for the life of the bird if the air sac is not healed. Birds that are afflicted with this permanent problem seem to lead happy but less active lives. In some instances, surgery may help to correct this problem.

8.37 Twisted, Discolored, or Deformed Feather Growth

Twisted feather growth is usually caused by some type of trauma to the feather follicle. Stunting can also induce this condition. Other common malformations are called trauma marks or lines. With the exception of these trauma induced abnormalities, most other malformations are caused by some type of malnutrition, malabsorption, or diseases as listed below.

8.37.1 Stress Bars

Dark lines whose length extend over the entire width of a feather are called stress bars. These bars are of varying width

Feather Abnormalities: #1-normal color and structure. #2-Poor overall coloration with malformed and missing barbs at point B. #3-Trauma lines at points A. #4-Overall dark discoloration showing black at point C. #5-Stress marks at points D

depending on how long the malnutrition continued. Poor nutrient absorption, which can be caused by disease, slow crop, or inadequate formulas causes stress bars to appear on the feathers. When the cause of the stress is remedied, normal feather development resumes.

8.37.2 Discoloration Bars

Discoloration bars appear as lines of color across the width of a feather, similar to stress bars. These are usually blue, blue-green, or red (candy-striping). The exact cause of this is unknown but they are probably linked to a period of improper nutritional absorption or some type of organ malfunction. These, as well as stress bars, are shed and replaced by normal feathers after the first moult.

8.37.3 Discolored Feathers

In green birds, the most common discoloration is the presence of yellow feathers. This can be caused by dietary deficiency or

Macaw wing feathers demonstrating the non-random pattern of dark discoloration bars.

organic malfunction which leads to poor nutrient absorption. A deficiency of the amino acid lysine or vitamin A are most often blamed for this discoloration. In diets that are not deficient in nutrients, yellow feathering can occur from an absorption problem in certain individuals. Fortunately, most of these problems correct themselves at the first moult. It is not known whether or not this trait can be genetic. After several generations of offspring have been produced, it will be interesting to review the history of each case.

In grey birds, we often see red or pink feathers instead of the normal grey color. This is thought to be caused by hampered nutrient absorption and is also reversed after the first moult. This condition causes no permanent health problems and most African Greys affected grow to be normal birds. It is interesting to note that this rarely occurs in parent-fed birds, only hand-reared babies.

Red feathers that appear orange are common in birds such as Eclectus and Amboina King parrots. Nutrient absorption is also blamed for these anomalies. In the case of Scarlet Macaws whose red feathers appear orange, it is usually the result of a poor hand feeding formula rather than absorption problems. The same can be said for the Blue and Gold Macaw whose blue appears to vary drastically throughout one individual feather.

Areas of black discoloration have been known to appear on the feathers of birds regardless of the proper color. The reason this occurs is not known but is most frequently seen in baby birds when using commercial hand rearing formulas. Although this is more common in Macaws (Blue and Gold), it has also been noticed in Amazons. A dietary change usually results in the normal coloration of feathers that have not yet developed.

8.37.4 Deformed Feathers

Deformed feathers can be described as feathers that do not fit together normally, have an abnormal shape to them, or are thin in appearance. In hand-fed babies these are usually caused by nutritional problems and many times accompany stunting syndrome. Often, feathers will appear to be overly narrow or have missing barbs which cause areas of transparency. All feather abnormalities are reversible, upon moult, with good health and proper diet.

When rearing species that are known to be susceptible to Psittacine Beak and Feather Syndrome, the appearance of twisted or malformed feathers should be a signal to isolate the bird and seek diagnosis. Papovavirus (Polyoma) will cause malformations of feathers also. These are the main forms of feather malformation that are caused directly by disease and are contagious. All other disease related abnormalities are a result of malnutrition that is caused by the illness, not necessarily the illness itself.

8.37.5 Trauma Lines

Trauma lines are many times mistaken for stress bars. They are caused by the preening (biting) of a feather that is still in the blood shaft and only partially developed. This results in injury to the feather and the line represents the scar from this injury. These lines seldom span the entire width of the feather. Trauma lines are most commonly seen on the tail feathers of macaws but can be found sporadically on different feathers with no set pattern and usually appear as thin lines. One over-zealous preener in a clutch can cause these lines to appear on all clutch mates.

Blue and Gold Macaw showing random pattern of trauma lines on feathers.

8.37.6 Twisted Feathers.

Feathers that emerge twisted from the shafts are usually a result of prior trauma (injury). If the feather follicle is permanently damaged, these feathers may emerge twisted for the life of the bird. Malformed feathers that cannot emerge from the follicle will continue to twist and collect under the skin. This is known as a feather cyst and requires medical attention.

8.38 Umbilical Problems

After hatching, a closed, dried umbilicus is seldom a problem. Unfortunately, many chicks hatch with what is commmonly called a wet umbilicus. This is much more common in cases where the eggs are artificially incubated.

Problems occur when the chick hatches with the umbilicus slightly open and raw tissue is exposed to the air. In some cases, this tissue actually extends outward from the navel. If bleeding is occurring, the area must be cauterized immediately or the chick may become weak and could possibly die. Use any clean cauterizing agent available for treatment of birds.

Once bleeding has stopped, the area will need to be cleaned to help prevent a bacterial invasion of exposed tissue. Using a piece of cotton, swab the area with a 1% *Betadine* solution. Treatment of these areas is recommended even if they appear to be dry and closed. This will aid the drying and sanitary closing of any exposed area that is too small to see. Within a few hours, the umbilical area should begin to dry and a scab will form. There is no need to continually treat the area when it has dried and healed over. This usually takes about twenty-four hours. Any strands that may extend from the umbilicus should not be pulled off as this may cause bleeding to restart. Allow these strands to dry completely and cut them or wait for them to fall off naturally.

If feces becomes caked in the umbilical area, do not try to pull it off. This area remains very delicate for about a week and is quite vulnerable to infection. If there is a need to remove dried feces, do this by using warm compresses and slowly working the mass free from the body. Usually the area is best left alone.

If the navel area is open to the extent that the internal yolk sac or intestines are exposed, there may be a need for minor surgery. Swab the area with *Betadine* and lubricate it with *KY Lubricating Jelly* to keep it moist until you can get the chick to a veterinarian who must decide whether or not to suture the area and begin antibiotic therapy.

Home treatment of less severe cases may include lubrication of the area with antibiotic ophthalmic ointments and bandaging of the navel. The area must remain moist so the skin can grow back over the exposed area. For this reason, fast healing medicines are not recommended. Any signs of inflammation or swelling should be brought to the attention of the veterinarian and antibiotic therapy should be started.

The umbilicus may close and pinch off a small portion of the yolk sac. This small *pea sized* yolk sac will remain outside of the abdomen, dry up, and eventually fall off. Larger sacs may need to be removed (see chapter 10.8). Care must be taken not to allow these sacs to be ruptured as bleeding will occur or peritonitis may ensue and the chick will become susceptible to infection. Never pull these dried sacs off of the chick as this will tear into the tissue below. This may worsen and further complicate the condition.

In all cases where the umbilicus is not healed over and dried after hatch, treat the area with *Betadine* solution. Keep these areas clean until healing is complete. Chicks are very vulnerable to infection when the umbilicus is wet and exposed. Swelling, oozing, or red inflammation is a sign of serious illness and chicks will usually need antibiotic therapy if they are to survive.

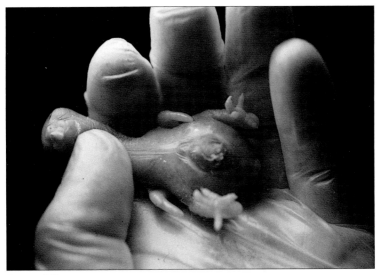

Open umbilicus.

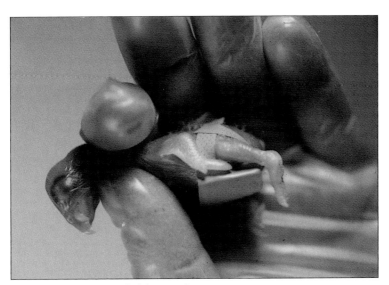

Loose butterfly bandage applied for protection.

Beginning of scab formation.

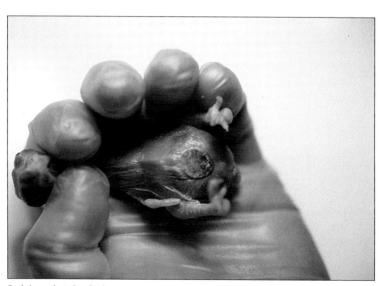

Scab is ready to be shed.

Healing is complete and navel has closed.

8.39 Viral Disease

The most potentially devastating problem that can enter a
nursery is a virus. The list of viral diseases that are known to
cause problems in psittacine nurseries is growing every year.
This is due to the greater number of birds being placed in captive
breeding programs. Many viral diseases are passed on by parent
carriers to their offspring during rearing. In rare cases there is
documentation of viruses being transmitted through the egg and
the chick may contract the disease before it has hatched. Many
times the disease is passed from chick to chick by the nursery
keeper. Proper hygiene may help curb many outbreaks.

One of the most common viral diseases that plagues psittacine
nurseries is called papova virus or polyomavirus. This disease
is so common that it is often called the *nursery disease*. It was
originally introduced to the United States aviculture by South
American Conures. It usually strikes birds when they undergo
the stress of feather growth. Symptoms of this virus include
hemorrhage under the skin, bruising, crop stasis and paling and
is usually followed by sudden death. The experimental use of
anti-viral drugs and immune system stimulants shows some
promise but has yet to prove effective. Carrier birds should be
identified and removed from production.

Phyrrhura chick exhibiting typical pox type lesions.

Confirmed diagnosis of a viral disease can only be made through histopathology. Although there are promising new tests on the horizon for ante-mortem diagnosis, organ and skin biopsies will have to be taken by your avian veterinarian and sent to a lab that has the capabilities to process them. These tests are very important as there is much to be learned about avian viruses.

Probably the second most prevalent viral disease to inflict the avian nursery is called Psittacine Beak and Feather Disease (PBFD). This virus most commonly affects Cockatoos and Eclectus parrots but has now been diagnosed in almost all other species especially when they have been housed with old world birds. It is a very contagious disease that often will show few symptoms in very young chicks. It is easier to identify in birds that are beginning to wean or have already weaned but it has been diagnosed in much older birds also. The long-term debilitating effects of this disease can be devastating, these include twisted or abnormal feather growth, lesions in the beak, constant bacterial infections and slow crops. It has also been noted that very young chicks that have not yet feathered will constantly cry for food even when the crop is full. The lack of feather down on birds that have feathered is another sign of trouble. Suspect birds should be isolated and tested by means of feather biopsies and histopathology.

There are several other diseases that may appear in the nursery. These seem to be viral in nature but have not yet been proven to be so. Among the most common are wasting syndrome (proventricular dilatation syndrome), bloating disease, viral serositis, and similar ailments all of which affect the digestive tract. Many times diseases that go undiagnosed and do not respond to antibiotic or anti-fungal treatment are assumed to be caused by underlying viruses.

8.40 Vomiting or Regurgitation of Food

There are a multitude of reasons why a baby will bring up the food in its crop. In many cases, regurgitation is a sign of an underlying problem. Baby parrots do not throw up food from a simple stomach ache. Anytime a chick regurgitates two feedings in a row, something must be done to rectify the situation. The following sections will explain certain circumstances that may cause vomiting of the crop contents.

8.40.1 During Weaning

Most baby parrots will begin to regurgitate a portion of their formula when they reach the weaning stage of development. Many babies will begin to feel uncomfortable with a full crop of formula and will regurgitate a small portion of it. This action can become a habit rather than a physical problem and some chicks will continue to bring up small portions of food even if the quantity fed is reduced. In cases like this, it is better to continue to feed the crop until it is full rather than half full. Many times the chick will only regurgitate half of the contents. If the chick allows half of the food to remain in the crop and is interested in the weaning foods that have been presented, there is little cause for alarm. When the chick regurgitates the entire contents of the crop on a continuous basis, there is a need for medical attention.

8.40.2 From Overfilling the Crop

When the crop is overfilled with formula the chick will often regurgitate for perfectly normal reasons. Most aviculturists consider any vomiting during the weaning stage as normal and probably due to overfilling. If the crop is too full, many chicks will vomit even if they are not yet at the weaning stage. Anytime a chick vomits the entire contents of the crop, they should be fed again after about thirty minutes. If the vomiting is repeated, there may be an underlying problem.

Some species of parrots have a greater propensity for vomiting portions of their food. One example is the African Grey parrot. Some Greys insist on bringing up at least 10% of their formula despite the amount of food given. This can begin when very young or occur during the pinfeather stage. In any case they seem to do it as a ritual and make quite a mess. This behavior has been reported by those that breed Eclectus parrots as well.

8.40.3 Courtship

It is normal for young parrots to mimic the courtship behavior of adult birds. This seems to be instinctual and can begin as young as the weaning age. This type of behavior is normal and is nothing to worry about. It can, however, become a nuisance.

8.40.4 From Medication

Often, vomiting in young chicks is caused by bitter or intolerable oral medications that have been added to the feeding formula. If vomiting persists, slightly reducing the dosage of medication may eliminate the problem. Consultation with your veterinarian is necessary whenever dosages are changed. The addition of some kind of sweetener to the formula may make it more palatable to the chick. In cases where it does not, the use of injectable medications may be warranted.

8.40.5 Sour Crop

In some cases, when food becomes too sour in the crop, it may trigger regurgitation. Although this can be considered a symptom of sour crop, it is usually an indicator of another problem such as a bacterial infection.

8.40.6 Fungal Infections

The overgrowth of yeast in the crop is one of the most common causes of regurgitation. If vomiting persists, a culture of the crop should be taken and analyzed.

8.40.7 Overheated or Cold Formula

If food is fed at an improper temperature, chicks may vomit to empty the crop. Regurgitation usually occurs immediately in this situation. Not all babies will vomit when fed hot food and this is the reason that burnt crops are so common. If hot food is accidentally fed, it is a good idea to feed cool food immediately to try and soothe the crop lining.

8.40.8 Intestinal Blockage

When the intestines become blocked, the formula backs up into the upper tract and crop. If the food sits in the crop long enough to sour, the chick may regurgitate and empty the crop. An intestinal blockage is very difficult to diagnose. Closely monitor the droppings of the chick. If only urates are present in the droppings or there are no droppings, a blockage should be suspected. Remember that some viruses can cause the droppings to contain only urates. In either case, there is a need for medical assistance. To the best of our knowledge, there is no surgical procedure to remove these blocks from the intestines. On several occasions, warm water has been forced up the cloaca and has successfully relieved a chick suffering from this ailment. In these cases, the blockage must have been very low in the tract, probably immediately inside of the cloacal opening.

If no formula is being digested at all, try feeding a liquid electrolyte solution as this may be able to slip past the blockage and may even help to eliminate it.

8.40.9 Intestinal Viruses

There are many unidentified viruses in the world of avian medicine. There exists one that can cause total digestive failure and, possibly, vomiting. It is believed to have been brought into the United States by imported babies from Honduras many years ago. The symptoms include crop stasis, no fecal matter in the droppings, a bloated abdomen and regurgitation. Although this virus cannot be cured, babies can recover from this ailment if they live through the seven-to fourteen-day critical period. The only hope is that you can maintain the chick on liquids long enough for the problem to subside. Dark, tarry droppings are normal if chicks are maintained on fluids exclusively. The chick is on the road to recovery when it can, once again, pass fecal matter.

8.40.10 Crop or Esophageal Injury

Injuries in the crop or esophagus may irritate the chick and cause regurgitation. Small quantities may need to be fed to keep the formula from irritating the affected area. When reducing quantity of formula, remember to increase the frequency of feeding so the chick does not lose too much weight. Thinner formulas tend to be less irritating to the chick and may curb their desire to vomit.

8.41 Yolk Sac Poisoning

Just prior to hatching, healthy, well-developed chicks draw the remainder of the yolk sac into the abdomen. The umbilicus closes around the yolk and internal organs to complete the incubation process that takes place in the egg. At this point the chick hatches.

Many aviculturists disagree as to what should be done about feeding at this point. Many times chicks seem to thrive better if feeding is withheld for a time after hatching. Personal research has shown that the problems involved in feeding a chick too soon after hatch are directly related to the amount of unabsorbed yolk within the abdomen. The translucent abdominal skin allows a reasonable view of the quantity of yolk that is still retained.

Chicks showing minimal or no visible areas of yellow to orange yolk under the skin can be fed immediately. Those with extensive areas of yellow-orange which represents a large quantity of retained yolk may need to have food withheld for twenty-four hours or more. Fluids can be given during this period to keep the chick hydrated. Many chicks seem to have no problem absorbing nutrients from the yolk as well as the formula being fed. In cases where there is a substantial amount of retained yolk, the mechanism that allows this yolk to be absorbed may be stopped or drastically slowed by the commencement of oral feeding. A chick such as this can at any time in the following week to ten days exhibit typical *failure to thrive* symptoms. The end result is crop stasis, extreme paling, and death. The shutdown of the yolk absorption process caused by the hand-feeding, creates a toxic situation.

Sometimes a chick suffering from this ailment can be saved by withholding formula and hoping that when the body requires nutrients, and the digestive system is empty, yolk absorption will resume. The difference in fecal matter between digested formula and digested yolk will make it apparent whether this tactic has been successful. When the digestive system runs out of formula, the dropping will cease to contain fecal matter and will consist of only white urates. If the yolk absorbing mechanism *kicks in*, you will begin to see tarry, translucent green droppings typical of yolk absorption. It may take several hours for this process to begin.

Once the tarry droppings resume, the bird can occasionally be given some oral electrolytes. You must wait until the tarry droppings cease for several hours and again only pure urates are passed before use of normal hand-feeding formula can be resumed.

Chances of yolk sac toxicity is greater if the remaining yolk that is visible is one-quarter of the abdominal area or more. Chicks that show 60-75 percent of the area filled with yolk are more likely to have the problem.

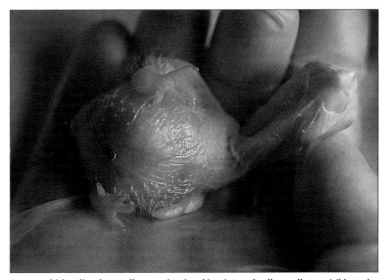

Amazon chick paling from yolk-sac poisoning. Note internal yellow yolk-sac visible under the skin.

Same chick after recovery. Note yellow yolk-sac under skin has disipated.

If after twenty-four hours the tarry *yolk* feces do not reappear with the white urates, the bird should be placed back on thin formula. If, at any time, the white urates cease to exist, the bird should be fed lactated ringers solution, *Pedialyte,* or *Ricelyte.*

Chapter 9
Non-Pathogenic Death

9.1 General

Non-pathogenic death refers to mortalities from causes other than disease agents. In adult birds this is a rarity with the exception of injury or trauma deaths. In the nursery, however, there are many more ways that death can occur. It is important not to use this fact as an excuse for high mortality in your nursery.

Chicks that die in the hand-feeding stage of life should have a necropsy performed on them. If cultures and examination reveal nothing it does not necessarily mean that a pathogen was not present at the time of death. There are numerous reasons why a pathogen cannot be located after death. If the carcass was stored or frozen prior to examination, the pathogen may have died also or if the chick died of a viral infection with no accompanying bacterial or fungal problems, the cause of death will not be visible by means of cultures or examination. The only way to diagnose a viral death is through histopathology using an electron microscope.

When a chick dies it should be rinsed well with cool water to counteract the insulating ability of the feathers. Once wet, place the bird in a sealable plastic bag and into the refrigerator. It may be beneficial to place it in the freezer for ten to twenty minutes to provide a quick chill and then move it to the refrigerator. Time is very important for proper diagnosis of the cause of death. The bird should be taken to the veterinarian immediately, then sent to the pathologist.

Never be complacent and assume that all deaths are non-pathogenic in nature, it is more beneficial to assume that a disease agent is present until it is proved otherwise. This will prompt the keeper to use proper sanitary measures and improved methods of hand-rearing.

9.2 Care Related Deaths

In the experience of the authors, improper care is the most common cause of death in babies that die at two weeks of age or less. This is the main reason this book was assembled, in an effort to standardize hand-feeding and dispel some of the ridiculous rumors and wives' tales. Hopefully, in the future, improper care and methodology will diminish. The two most prevalent types of improper care are malnutrition and improper brooding.

9.2.1 Malnutrition

Chicks that are fed improper quantities of food, insufficient frequencies of feeding, or inadequate diets can suffer from malnutrition. Diets may be too low in necessary nutrients or too high in those that are potentially toxic. Deaths that occur from these reasons are avoidable.

This book outlines recommendations as to quantity and frequency of feeding. The methods outlined have proved themselves time and time again through many years of experience with, literally, thousands of chicks. Diet recommendations are variable at this time due to the lack of research that has been performed and the many different ways to supply the same nutrients.

There is a fair amount of research being performed at this time and we are sure it will yield some very fine products in the near future. Meanwhile, it is best to stick with a diet that has proven itself for those that have raised many parrot chicks. If a formula is marginal, the problems that it yields will surface only rarely. For someone who is raising only three or four babies a year the problems may never surface. If hundreds of chicks are fed yearly, chances are that the problems caused by these formulas will surface regularly. This is also true of quality control and consistent product manufacturing. If a product varies in its contents it will only be noticed by those that use it in large quantities. At the present time, if you need consistent results, it is wise to prepare your own formula from proven recipes.

9.2.2 Improper Brooding

The result of incorrect brooding can mimic that of malnutrition. This is partly due to the fact that inaccurate brooding causes inefficient digestion and in turn, malnutrition. Methods of brooding and brooding temperature should be investigated before the blame for malnutrition is placed on dietary factors.

9.3 Mechanical Deaths

Any death that occurs because of the misuse of a tool, handler error, or other accidental physical injury, can be considered mechanical death. Even the most experienced aviculturist will make a fatal error once in a while. The lesson is only learned if precautions are taken to help prevent the same accident from happening again.

9.3.1 Injury from Feeding

Feeding injuries usually result from the misuse of a feeding tube or gavage. The improper use of a feeding tube can lead to a punctured crop or esophagus. If a major blood supply is also involved, death will follow. Once punctures of the esophagus or crop occur, food leaks into the body cavity and infection develops. It may take several days for the symptoms to indicate this problem and by this time the chick may be critically ill.

9.3.2 Injury from Physical Accidents

Accidents do happen but this is no excuse to leave a young, active chick unattended where it can fall to the floor and injure itself. Experienced aviculturists learn never to turn their backs on a chick that is not secure in its brooder or brooding container. The older chicks tend to take a fall better, but any fall can cause irreversible internal damage to babies.

As the nestlings mature and begin to exercise, they may take their first flight, crashing into a window or mirror. At best, they will experience a loss of equilibrium and will stumble about for a moment. Central nervous system damage can occur and the chick will exhibit the same symptoms as it would if a virus had attacked its system. Head shaking, tremors, and vomiting are a sign that damage is extensive and the bird needs to be evaluated by an avian veterinarian.

9.3.3 Aspiration

The term aspiration applies to the inhalation of formula into the lungs. It may occur from improper feeding or when a nest-mate pushes or walks across a full crop of food. If aspiration death is suspected a necropsy needs to be performed on the chick to determine if this is the real cause of death. When a chick dies with a full crop of formula, the liquid food may come up the esophagus and dribble into the trachea. This appears to be an aspiration death when, in fact, it was not. If the lungs are affected upon examination of the bird, it is a reasonable assumption that aspiration or the associated pneumonia may have caused the death. If the entire respiratory system seems to be unaffected other causes of death should be investigated.

9.4 Congenital Deaths

Deaths that are predetermined by the genetic background of the chick are called congenital. Chicks that are born with these inherent problems usually do not survive for very long and many die before being hatched. As nature would have it, the weak or abnormal genes that are passed on to some chicks are a sure death sentence.

Some of the problems that have been surmised as congenital range from an exposed spinal column or heart to nutrient absorption problems that will cause a chick to succumb in as little as a week. True *failure to thrive* cases are a congenital problem related to poor nutrient absorption. Incompatible, poor, or weak genes are blamed, frequently, for deaths that occur from poor brooding or feeding practices.

9.4.1 Liver or Kidney Failure

On rare occasions organic congenital defects do occur and will many times involve the liver or the kidneys. Signs of this disorder include jaundice and yellow urates. Chicks that hatch with a yellow hue to the skin may be very normal and will usually become a pinkish, yellow color in a few days. This is very common in newly hatched Cockatoos. If jaundice occurs several days after hatching or intensifies as time goes on, there may be a problem. Kidney problems are often indicated by the presence of few or no normal urates in the droppings. Large quantities of clear liquid may also be present. This will result in dehydration and eventual death if the body cannot resolve the problem in a reasonably short period of time.

9.4.2 Lethal Genes

Lethal genes are very difficult to diagnose. If they are a part of parrot mortality, they play a very small role. They have surfaced in canaries that have been inbred for albinism. Any canaries that carry the albino gene may also carry the combination of genes that predispose the chicks to death soon after hatching.

9.5 Poisoning

On rare occasions chicks have been suspected of having ingested plants or other toxins that cause their deaths. The authors agree that plants or anything that may be toxic should not be within reach of parrot chicks, as they will play with them and mouth them in a natural manner. Different chicks or species of chicks may have disparate tolerances to certain plants or substances. Our knowledge of toxins are based on heresay and stories that have been handed down from one breeder to another. There are, however, two causes of death that can be substantiated. These are listed below.

9.5.1 Teflon Poisoning

The overheating of teflon and teflon-type coated cookware has probably caused the death of more baby birds than any other toxin. When this type of cookware is heated empty, it releases a gas that is extremely toxic to birds. For this reason it is recommended that no pans containing a non-stick surface be used in or around the nursery. Horror stories involving this toxin usually include a pot of formula put on the stove to heat and the phone ringing in another room. After leaving for several minutes to talk with a friend, the nursery keeper returns to find all of the chicks dead or near death. It may be convenient to use a teflon pan to boil formula, but the consequences will outweigh the benefits.

9.5.2 Toxic Reaction to Wormer Medicines

Some anti-parasitic drugs that are commonly used to treat adult breeding stock may be toxic if fed to baby parrots. The preparations that have been indicated as a problem usually contain the drug called *Mebendazole*. Apparently filling the crop with formula containing the recommended dosage of *Mebendazole* is different than flock treating adult parrots with the same medication. This could be due to the fact that the drug is usually administered in the water and is consumed over a period of time. If it is fed to a chick, it will pass through the system very quickly, thus possibly overdosing the chick. There should be no reason to worm domestically produced babies if the parent stock have been treated correctly for these parasites. If parent fed chicks do need to be wormed, investigate which drugs and the dosages have been used safely in the past.

Chapter 10
Medical Procedures for the Aviculturist

10.1 General Information

It is very important for the aviculturist to learn the procedures explained in this chapter. This is not to imply that they are better performed by the breeder than the veterinarian or vice versa, but many times the need to treat a chick immediately must take priority. Chicks that break bones, swallow feeding tubes, get something in their eyes, or are born with extended yolk sacs must be attended to without delay. If professional aviculturists are to be self-sufficient, they must have the resolve and knowledge to deal with these problems without the assistance of professional medical personnel.

Whenever possible, the administration of medication should be handled by the aviculturist. Chicks tend to respond better to treatment if it is performed in familiar surroundings and by someone they recognize. It is important that the breeder follow the instructions outlined by trained and competent avian specialists.

10.2 Removing Foreign Objects From The Crop

When something is ingested into the crop by accident, it needs to be removed so it does not disrupt the digestive process of the chick. In their fervor to feed, chicks will often swallow anything that enters their mouths.

The most commonly ingested items are wood shavings, corn cob bedding, feeding tubes, and large pieces of fruit or vegetables. Some of these are easy to remove but require a two-person team. One person holds the chick upright, gently stretching the head and neck upwards. The second person must carefully manipulate the foreign object upward towards the entrance to the crop. As the obstruction becomes visible in the back of the mouth, a blunt pair of forceps, hemostats, or small pair of needle-nosed pliers, can be used to remove it.

These procedures are very stressful to young chicks and often cause an increase in respiration and breathing. Because of this, care must be taken not to force liquid food up into the mouth or the chick may aspirate. It is recommended that the crop be emptied of formula before any manipulation of the foreign objects takes place, see the following section 10.3. If you have any doubt as to your ability to remove the obstruction from the crop, consult an avian veterinarian for assistance.

Feeding tubes that are cut too short can disconnect from the syringe and slide into the crop of the chick. If the tube is long enough that a portion is still visible in the mouth, it is easily removed by grasping the exposed piece and pulling it out. Tubes that are cut very short may enter the crop entirely. These must be manipulated with the fingers from outside of the crop and worked into a vertical position before being forced up and out of the esophagus.

Chicks that are weaning and just beginning to learn how to eat, may swallow whole grapes or large pieces of fruit or vegetables. If this food is soft enough to be manually reduced into small pieces from outside of the crop, they will pass it into the digestive system with no problem. However, if they are hard pieces that are too large to enter the digestive tract, they may block the entrance to the proventiculus and cause digestion to cease. The obstruction must be manipulated manually from outside the crop until it can be pushed up the neck and into the mouth. Use forceps or small needle-nosed pliers to remove them from the mouth.

Severe impaction, where an entire crop full of unshelled seed or bedding material has been swallowed, may need to be surgically removed. Crop surgery must be performed to remove the obstructing material by an avian surgeon who has the necessary experience. A diet evaluation is in order whenever chicks eat large quantities of bedding material. This is usually an indication that they are not receiving the required nutrients and remain constantly hungry either because of deficient formulas, or insufficient quantities or frequencies of feeding.

10.3 How to Empty the Crop

When the crop stops pushing food into the digestive tract, it may sour and needs to be emptied manually. This can only be done with a tube that is long enough to reach into the crop and vacuum out the contents. The procedure is the same as for force feeding but the food is sucked out instead of added to the crop.

To *pull the crop*, may require two people. One person must restrain the chick as the other gently introduces the tube, which has been lubricated with water or a water soluble lubricant, into the crop and withdraws the food. The first person must stretch the bird's head and neck while controlling the feet and wings from flailing around. If the holder can manage to place one finger lightly over the neck, in the area of the esophagus, they will be able to feel the tube entering the crop or feel for two tubes, one which is the trachea and the other which is the feeding tube in the esophagus. This will alert the second person that the tube is in the right place.

Using the syringe and tube, it may be helpful to inject a few milliliters of warm water into the crop and massage it into the thickened food. This will facilitate extraction of the crop contents. Before withdrawing on the plunger of the syringe, be sure the end of the tube is positioned in the center of the food that needs to come out and not against the crop wall. Otherwise damage may occur to the crop lining. It is easy to feel the tube and the location of the tip by using your fingers on the outside of the crop. Do not push too hard or the food may be forced into the mouth.

Continue adding water and withdrawing the old food until the liquid that is withdrawn is clean. Always be careful not to suck up the lining of the crop into the end of the tube. The lining of the crop is delicate and damage can occur. Withdraw the contents very slowly and stop if any resistance is felt. This could be due to the crop lining blocking the opening of the tube. Reposition the tube toward the center of the crop and continue to vacuum the liquid out.

Larger pieces of food will not come out using the tube. It may be helpful to mix some digestive enzymes with warm water and feed them to the chick. This will soften the food and start to pre-digest it. Once the food is thin enough to withdraw, follow the instructions above.

10.4 Restraining Chicks Safely

A picture is worth a thousand words when trying to explain how to safely hold chicks of different ages. Study the pictures that are included on this subject. Notice that the areas of concern are the head, legs, and wings. Depending on the reason that the chick needs to be restrained, the hold may vary a bit to control one or more of these areas.

Chicks have a knack for reaching up and grabbing the syringe out of your hand when you are trying to give an injection. This is not only annoying, but may also injure the chick if the needle is torn from the injection site. If there is no one to hold the chick for an injection, the easiest method of restraint is to hold the baby's head with one hand and press its feet against your stomach. Use your forearm to support the chick's body. The chick will usually hold on to your shirt with its feet and the injection can be given safely. Ensure that pressure is not applied against a full crop during this procedure, otherwise aspiration may occur.

Babies that climb on the sides of the wire cages can be injected by pressing them against the wire where they cannot move, again ensuring pressure is not applied to the crop. The needle is inserted through the wire and into the muscle tissue. Care must be taken not to allow them to flinch and bend the needle after it has been inserted. This same method can be used if a chick must be tube fed and there is no assistant to help with the restraint. Proficiency at injecting or tube feeding is an absolute must before trying to perform either procedure through the bars or wires of a cage.

This hold offers excellent control for force feeding. Note, wing tips held with legs. Neck is extended and the thumb is on the jaw, not the neck. This facilitates entry of tube into esophagus.

Holding chick tightly against chest will control legs so injections can be given without an assistant.

Excellent hold for injection when assistance is available. Left hand controls head, neck, wings and upper body. Right hand controls legs. Note that no pressure is applied on the full crop.

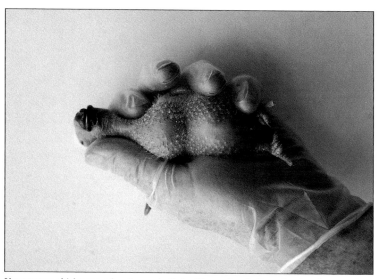

Very young chicks can often be controlled with one hand. Note the thumb on neck to limit the ability of the chick to wiggle.

Some older chicks will reach up to grab the syringe with their foot. Note left foot is restrained between fingers.

When restraining a baby to force-feed it, always remember not to put pressure on the esophagus and inadvertently pinch it closed. When holding the head of a chick it is very easy to slide the fingers down the neck, pinch off the esophagus and make insertion of the tube impossible. Be sure not to push on the crop as the food will only be forced back up the esophagus and into the mouth. This creates a possibility of aspiration. Whenever restraint is necessary with hand-feeding babies, check the amount of food present in the crop and be aware not to put pressure on it.

Holding a chick's head and allowing the body and legs to flail is dangerous. Chicks may injure themselves by twisting the body while you maintain the head in one position.

Most accidents that occur from restraint are caused when the handler is afraid to put enough pressure on the bird. Most beginners are shocked at how much force is required to restrain a flailing baby. Birds, unlike mammals, are almost impossible to strangle by holding the neck too tight. It is easy to bruise the neck but difficult to actually squeeze the trachea (or windpipe) closed.

10.5 Correcting Crooked Beaks

The greatest percentage of crooked beaks are reversible if recognized and treated in the early stages of misalignment. There have been some attempts at splinting these beak deformities in young chicks which has yielded variable results. Some veterinarians use some special apparatus and an Elizabethan collar. This seems a bit stressful and unnecessary if daily physical therapy can effect a cure, but in some cases it must be done.

When hand-rearing parrot chicks, it is necessary to be observant at all times. When any slight deviation of the beak becomes apparent, therapy should be started to correct the problem. Physical therapy should be done at least five times a day if it is to inhibit an unnatural growth pattern in the beak.

The usual method of beak correction is to place the thumb and forefinger of one hand on the upper beak just below the nares. Using the thumb and forefinger of the other hand, gently push the tip of the beak towards the correct position. If there seems to be a little movement in the beak, the therapy should do the job eventually. Constant readjustment must be done or the beak will continue to grow in the wrong direction.

Therapy sessions are performed about five times a day for very short periods of time. Push the tip in the right direction and hold it there for a few seconds. Repeat this procedure as often as possible over the course of a minute or two without causing alarm or stress to the chick, this would constitute one complete session. It may be necessary to force the tip of the beak beyond the correct position in order for it to spring back and remain in the spot where you want it.

Crooked beaks that are not corrected in time or have deviated too far to one side, create yet another problem. The side of the front tip of the lower mandible will overgrow in the upward direction. This is due to the fact that properly fitted beaks abrade each other and keep the edges from overgrowing. If the lower mandible does not fit into the inside ridge of the upper beak, it will continue to grow until it has been ground down manually. If uncorrected, this overgrown lower mandible will continue to push the upper beak further out of alignment.

Grinding the lower mandible into shape, combined with the therapy on the upper beak may help to correct the problem. Sometimes it is necessary to overgrind the lower mandible on the side that is overgrown. This causes the normal side of the lower mandible to put pressure on the upper beak in just the right direction. Once the upper beak is in the proper position, the lower will not grow out abnormally. It may take only a few trimmings to correct the problem or it may take many. Depending on the age of the chick and the amount of elasticity that remains in the upper beak, the lower mandible may require trimming indefinitely.

In this situation as in many, prevention is easier than the cure. When feeding young chicks, try to pay attention to the alignment of the beak and perform the physical therapy needed to keep upper and lower beak in line.

10.6 Removing Obstructions from the Eye

When using wood shavings or some similar substrate in brooding containers, dust can get into the eyes of the chicks. If untreated, an infection under the eyelids may result and in severe cases may cause abnormal eye development or even blindness.

There are liquid eyewash preparations available for use in small children. These preparations usually come in a squirt-type bottle that make it easy to project the liquid in the desired location. If this is unavailable, sterile water or physiological saline can be projected through a syringe using a large gauge needle. The idea is to flood the eye with clean liquid to wash out the foreign material.

The easiest way to do this is to hold the chick on its side and tilt the head slightly downwards with the affected eye up. Direct the flow of the cleansing liquid into the eye allowing the overflow to roll off of the chick's head. If an assistant is present to help, he can gently lift the eyelid to assure that the liquid flushes the eye completely.

Eyes that have been scratched or are ulcerated, should not be treated as described above. These cases require the use of special ophthalmic preparations to help the cornea heal. If you are unsure as to what is required, consult with an avian specialist for advice.

10.7 Splinting a Broken Wing or Leg

Broken wings or legs need to be attended to immediately. The sooner the break is set the more rapidly it will heal. If professional help is required, the break should be taped to keep it from moving around and causing more damage to surrounding tissues until the bird can be delivered to the veterinarian. The procedures below are not recommended for the aviculturist unless there is no possible way to have the bird examined by a veterinarin. If bones are set incorrectly they will heal incorrectly and will need to be re-broken and set again. The only way to diagnose and properly treat some of the serious broken bone problems is through the use of x-rays. If the bones extend through the skin or there is considerable swelling and tissue damage, an avian veterinarian should be contacted immediately.

If the break is a simple fracture and must be treated at home, the following is a suggested method of treatment. Any complications that may be noticed should be referred to a veterinarian. When the break is in the leg, tape it in the folded position against the breast of the bird. There is a product called *Vet-wrap* that sticks only to itself and not to the skin or feathers. *Vet-wrap* can be used to temporarily position the broken leg. The tape is to keep the chick from putting weight on the break. This is only a temporary measure and the injury must be treated as soon as possible. Time is of the essence as the bones may begin to heal in the wrong position if treatment is delayed for too long.

If you choose to set and splint the break yourself, it will require the use of an assistant to steady the chick. The materials needed are tape and a tongue depressor or popsicle stick. When treating small birds only wide, stiff tape may be needed as the tape itself will support the break. There are a few different types of tape that will work. Masking tape or some of the paper tapes that adhere to themselves, but not to the skin, are best. If the chick insists on chewing the tape, place a layer of silver duct tape over the others since the chicks do not like to chew this type of tape. There are many ways to splint broken bones and the best way will only be known through experience.

The wooden tongue depressor or stick must be trimmed to the proper size. If the break is in the femur (the upper part of the leg), the stick should be cut so that it does not extend below the joint or protrude upwards into the chick's abdomen. Gently feel the two sections of bone and try to align them as well as possible. Place one stick on the inside of the leg and one on the outside over the break. This keeps the break from flexing in either direction. Once the sticks are in position, wrap the leg and splints in tape to keep the broken sections of the leg from bending. The splint must be wrapped tightly but care must be taken not to cut off the circulation to the foot. If the foot changes color or becomes cold to the touch, the bandage is too tight. It is often helpful to tape the splinted leg to the body of the chick so it cannot be used for a few days. Position the leg in the natural folded position before taping. The leg can be freed from the body in a few days but the splinted section must remain taped in order for the bones to heal. It normally takes about seven to ten days for a bone to heal well enough to remove the splint.

If the broken bone is in the tibia (lower leg), the splint sticks should be made a little longer than those for the femur. When splinting the tibia, allow the stick to extend a bit past the foot. When the chick puts weight on the broken leg, the stick will absorb the pressure. As stated above, it is still recommended that the broken leg be folded and taped to the birds body for a couple of days. Once the leg is released, the chick will walk on the extended sections of the splints and will not be able to put pressure on the break.

When the break is in the ankle, the splint sticks must also extend past the foot as described above. This is very important for healing purposes. It may also be helpful to house all chicks with broken legs in small, almost tightly fitted containers. This will restrict the movement of the chick. Once acclimated to the container, they will usually lean against the sides to rest. Chicks suffering from splayed legs will also benefit by being placed in tight containers such as these. It will keep the legs in the desired position for optimum healing.

Broken wings are more difficult to splint or tape than breaks in the legs. However, the taping is a bit less critical because the bird cannot place weight on the break. In most cases, limiting the use of the wing is all that is necessary to mend the bones properly. If the bones are aligned, the wing need only be taped in the closed, folded position and then taped again to the body. Be sure to wrap the body tape all the way around the bird so the wing cannot be extended. Some wings droop permanently after healing. This is true of those that are set by professionals as well as those that are set at home. If the droop does hamper the bird's ability to fly, it is of little consequence. As with broken legs, the wing may take seven to ten days to heal before the bandages can be removed.

10.8 Tying Off An Extended Yolk Sac

As the artificial incubation of parrot eggs becomes more commonplace, the chances of chicks hatching with unabsorbed yolks increase. If the yolk that is exterior to the body is large, it will not be absorbed by the chick and may become infected with bacteria or rupture and kill the chick. There is a surgical procedure to remove these external yolk sacs but, in severe cases, the survival rate is low.

If a chick hatches with an external yolk sac that is the size of a small pea or smaller, there is rarely a need for surgical removal. This sac usually dries up and falls off, similar to the umbilical cord of a human child. The area must be kept clean and the sac treated with some type of topical antibacterial ointment or solution. Trauma to the area may cause severe bleeding so chicks must be protected until the sac falls off. Never pull at the healing area in an attempt to remove the extension as this will only further complicate the situation.

Large yolk sacs must be tied off and removed. The most common complication to this surgery occurs when the intestines are also exposed and they are accidentally tied off and cut with the yolk sac. Chicks cannot recover from this type of accident. The normal procedure is to loop a piece of absorbent suture material around the external yolk sac and pull it tight enough to make a seal between the yolk and the chick's abdomen. Be careful not to pull so tightly that the suture cuts into the sac and causes it to rupture. Once the yolk sac is tied off from the body, the sac is cut away just slightly to the outside of the suture. Treat the area with antibacterial ointments and allow the remainder of the sac to dry up and fall off as described above. The chick may benefit from fluid or antibiotic therapy during the healing process.

10.9 Administration of Medication

General:

Having the knowledge and skills necessary to administer medication can be a valuable asset. A major part of successfully returning an infirmed baby bird to good health is the proper administration of medication. When medication is prescribed twice a day, that means every 12 hours. When it is prescribed three times a day, that means every eight hours. Care must be given to keep the time intervals between doses as similar as possible. Most medications are effective only if the right blood levels are attained and maintained for a sufficient period of time. If the amount of medication in the bloodstream is allowed to periodically drop to low levels, you could wind up with a major problem. Insufficient dosing or treatment periods may result in the overgrowth of resistant strains of bacteria. This could be fatal. For this reason it is almost as important to have proper time intervals between treatments as it is to use correct doses. This does not mean that when the prescribed frequency of treatments is twice a day, that they have to be exactly twelve hours apart. If out of necessity, the timing must be ten and fourteen hours apart it will probably not cause a problem. If, however, they become eight and sixteen hours apart in a twenty-four hour period, then a problem may result. Some medications, such as those used for fungal infections in the mouth and crop, do not depend on blood levels to effect a cure. They depend on repetitive contact between the medication and the fungal growth. With these types of medications, frequent application will result in faster healing.

In all cases, medications should be administered for the entire time period that is prescribed by your veterinarian. In some cases, a bird may appear to be 100% cured after the first three or four days of a seven to ten day treatment regimen. Some people make the mistake of ceasing treatment or becoming less concerned about treating at the time of apparent recovery. This can be a major mistake. This may not only lead to a relapse, but it could allow for the overgrowth of resistant strains.

The three ways that medication can be used are topically, orally, and by injection. Remember that your veterinarian will prescribe a system that is sensible according to the information available. If the facts change it might be necessary to change the method of treatment. If for example, it is decided that you will treat your bird orally with an antibiotic to combat a bacterial infection in the digestive tract, and when you bring it home you discover that the chick has stopped passing food out of the crop, it should be obvious that the facts have changed and oral administration will not work. Anytime you have new information, provide this to the veterinarian so he can make a decision as to the best mode of treatment.

10.9.1 Topical Application of Medication

Topical application refers to the application of medication on the external surface of the body. Continual contact with the medication is what kills the responsible organism. In most cases, it is some type of ointment or lotion that is applied to the problem areas. It is important to remember that, like sun block or sun tan lotion, if it has been rubbed or washed off it will not work. Constant re-application is essential for a rapid cure. Some medications that are taken orally for fungal infections actually work in a topical way. *Nystatin* or *Nolvasan* solution may be used in the mouth in order to kill fungal growth that is confined to that area. Although you are placing the medication in the bird's mouth, it is working as a topical medicine to cure the infection. In cases such as this, the more often the application the more rapid the cure. *Nystatin* solution placed into the crop in order to kill off fungal infection in the crop and the lower digestive tract also works in a topical way. It is important to have *Nystatin* in the digestive tract at all times in order to effect a rapid cure. The more constant the contact the *Nystatin* has with the fungus, the quicker it will destroy it. For this reason it is advisable to dose with the *Nystatin* on an empty crop prior to feeding. This gives it a chance to coat the lining of the crop and parts of the lower tract without being diluted with formula. In the case of injuries, some topical ointments may be better suited than others. In instances where rapid closing, drying and healing are very desirable your veterinarian might wish you to use an ointment such as *Panalog*. This will dry the wound and cause rapid healing. If however there is damage to areas of the beak or skin that will need the time to re-grow in the injured area, then a slower healing, more moisturizing type ointment such as *Nolvasan* ointment might be preferred. The more rapid the healing capacity of the ointment, the more the possibility of scarring. Cotton swabs are usually used to apply most of these topical ointments.

Also included as topical applications are the use of nose drops, eye drops, or ophthalmic ointments. Nose drops are sometimes prescribed for birds that have a slight case of non-specific sinusitis. This is most commonly an antibiotic eye drop that is placed in the nares several times a day. It is important to remove any loose mucous from the nostrils before use. The medication will not be able to penetrate the sinus cavity if it is clogged with mucous. Loose mucous can be sucked out of the nostrils by using a syringe. Place the open tip over the nostril and draw up the plunger to create the suction necessary to evacuate any fluids. In the case of eye problems, your veterinarian will usually prescribe an ointment or drops. Sometimes, you may wish to use a drug available in powder form. Whatever the case, we have found that cures are effected more rapidly when the treatment is used three or four times a day instead of once or twice.

If eyelids have become pasted shut, they must be soaked with warm compresses until they can be gently pulled open. Only if the medication comes in direct contact with the eyeball can you be assured that there will be total coverage of all areas of the eye and the surrounding tissues. The warmth of the eye will melt an ointment and the fluids in the eye will carry the medication to all affected areas. Placing medication on an eye that is pasted shut is futile and usually has no medicinal value.

10.9.2 Oral Administration of Medication

Since the scope of this book concerns itself with the care of babies that are unweaned or weaning, we will not go into great detail on the use of medication that is administered in the drinking water. In order for water treatments to be effective, the chicks must be old enough to be drinking the water. In weaning birds that need to be treated for a mild yeast problem, a mild *Nolvasan* solution can be made (1 tablespoon to one gallon of water) and given daily. This preparation can be used as a preventative also. Even if chicks do not drink the water, they will almost always play in it and, in effect, topically treat themselves. Most treatment regimens in young babies involve the mixing of the medication with the formula or feeding it directly into the crop.

When a medication has to be mixed with the formula, it is important to let your veterinarian know how much formula the baby digests in a twenty-four hour period. This information will enable him to adjust the dosage for exactly the bird or birds that you are medicating. If you do not know this information, the veterinarian may be forced to guess.

A more effective method of treatment is to place the exact amount of medication that is prescribed directly into the crop with the use of a feeding tube or a gavage. Smaller chicks that have a strong feeding response will usually drink the medication directly from the syringe if it is not too bitter in taste or too cool in temperature. When mixing medication with your formula do not add the medication until the mix has cooled to serving temperature. High heat can destroy the effectiveness of certain drugs. Whenever a bird is being treated with oral antibiotics and the crop slows considerably or stops completely, a veterinarian should be consulted concerning a change in the course of treatment.

10.9.3 Injections

Administration of medication by injection can be performed in one of three methods. The first and most often used is intramuscular (IM). This is something that everyone can do with minimal instruction if they have the confidence to try. The very tiny needles available for insulin users are ideal for young chicks. Using these small needles makes the task easy and virtually painless if the bird is properly restrained. Injections should be made in the plumpest part of the breast surrounding the keel bone. If an intramuscular injection is necessary on a very small chick that has not yet developed much breast muscle, the injection can be done very carefully in the thigh muscle or, preferably, subcutaneously if possible. The precise dosage must be known before any injection is given. One big advantage of injections is that they will deliver the medicine to the system even if the crop is not functioning and no food is being digested.

The second type of injection is called subcutaneous or simply *sub-Q*. The term means *beneath the skin*. This is precisely how the injection is done. Subcutaneous injections are the most common way to rehydrate a chick that needs fluids. This is probably due to the fact that fluids injected directly under the skin will be absorbed into the body in a very short period of time. Performing this procedure is quite easy. The needle is inserted into the skin at an angle so as to not penetrate the muscle wall underneath. Fluid is injected under the skin to form a bubble. It is easier to position the needle properly if the skin at the injection site is loose and flexible, such as behind the neck on the upper back and in the webs of the legs where the thighs connect to the body. One must take care not to inject fluids into the airsacs of the chick as this can cause many problems.

The final method of injection is called intravenous or (IV) injection. Using this method, the medicine or fluids are injected directly into the blood stream. It is the most difficult of all to do as the blood vessels of the chicks are very tiny and have a tendency to move away from the needle. If an IV injection is necessary, it may be best to contact an avian veterinarian at once. These injections are most often used in cases of severe dehydration or where medication must reach the system immediately. *Lactated ringers* solution is the most often used fluid. Occasionally there is a need to add a minute amount of *Dextrose* or other types of fluids. In some cases, with this type of therapy, recovery from severe dehydration is almost immediate.

Chapter 11
Weaning

11.1 General Information

The transformation period where a chick becomes less dependent on hand-feeding and begins eating solid foods could be the most important period of its life. Weaning is an unpredictable time and often features weight loss, illness, depression, or personality changes. These problems make weaning a stressful and difficult time.

11.2 When Does Weaning Begin?

The question of when to begin weaning a chick has many answers. When dealing with species such as the Lories and Lorikeets, weaning can be started and finished in as little as one day. These gregarious parrots need only to be placed in a small cage with a bowl of warm formula or nectar and will usually eat by themselves in a very short period of time. Placing the spoon or a familiar feeding instrument in the bowl of formula helps to teach the bird where to look for food. If young birds that are already weaned are gentle enough to be in the same cage with weaning birds, the process will be rapid as the weaned birds teach the others how to eat. Lories and Lorikeets may begin to eat on their own when their tail feathers have grown to half the length of the adults. At this time they can be moved to the weaning cages and monitored closely to assure they do not starve to death.

Larger birds such as Cockatoos, Macaws, or Amazons should be provided with fruits, vegetables, and bowls of formula when they begin to pick up and mouth objects around them. If provided with weaning foods when they are about half feathered, they will often be eating by the time the feathering is completed.

This bin containing ten different types of Amazons is being transported to weaning cages.

11.3 How to Proceed with Weaning

Once a chick is old enough to pick at food, a variety of soft foods such as vegetables, fruits, and soaked monkey biscuits can be placed in small dishes in the brooding buckets. Chicks will generally not eat sufficient quantities to sustain themselves and hand-feeding should continue until they can maintain their weight on their own.

A list of common food items to offer during the weaning process is listed below. Certain birds are like children as they will develop a taste for some things and totally ignore others. This is perfectly normal. If a chick seems to enjoy eating a certain item, more of this particular food should be offered to encourage it to continue eating. When feeding vegetable items, it is sometimes helpful to steam them in the microwave for a few minutes to make them more appetizing. This is particularly true of sweet potatoes, carrots, or even pieces of apple.

Offer:

1. Apple, pears, plums, oranges, cranberries, papaya, melons, or almost any fruits (no pits or seeds except those that come from the melons as the others may be toxic).

2. Soaked monkey biscuits (warmed in the microwave), bread, breakfast cereals such as cheerios or fruit loops. Be careful as grain foods may spoil and should be replaced with fresh food every four hours.

3. Vegetables such as broccoli, carrots, sweet potatoes, squashes, pumpkin, parsley, leaf lettuce, spinach, endive or chickory, and virtually all others.

4. Offer seeds such as sunflower, millet, spray millet, hemp, or canary seeds. In the beginning it may be helpful to wet the seeds before giving it to the chick. Be careful not to let any foodstuff go rancid or spoil.

Weaning continues as the chick eats more and more by itself. As the consumption of weaning food increases, slowly decrease the amount and frequency of hand-feeding. It is normal for chicks to loose weight during weaning but it must be closely monitored to assure the chick does not get too thin (see section 11.7).

Larger species of birds may take from two to five weeks to wean completely from hand-feeding. Hyacinth Macaws have been known to take up to twice as long as the other macaws but this is not actually necessary and they will wean at a younger age. When weaning Hyacinth Macaws or the other larger Macaws, pieces of soaked, warm monkey biscuit can be placed

Presentation of food at an early age will help to facilitate weaning.

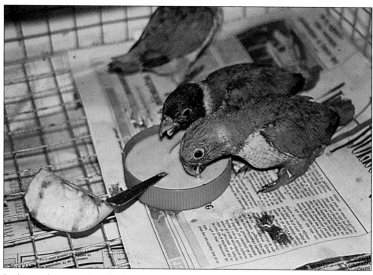

Lories can be weaned easily if presented with a dish of formula.

in the mouth and the feeding response elicited to cause swallowing. In this way, the feeder physically teaches the bird that food is to be swallowed. After each teaching session, a bowl of the same soaked biscuits should be left in the cage so the bird can get to it. This procedure may also be helpful when dealing with other species of parrots. Once the chicks begin to swallow food from the bowl, weaning should proceed at an accelerated rate. Water is offered when the chicks are being hand-fed only once or twice a day. Always introduce water in shallow bowls so chicks do not accidentally drown themselves.

Continue to offer fresh food and reduce hand-feeding as the chicks learn to eat. The last formula feed of the day should not be eliminated unless the bird has a full crop of weaning foods at the normal feeding time. Patience is vital as these chicks are dependent on hand-feeding and need to remain strong if they are to wean and thrive.

11.4 When is a Bird Weaned?

A chick is completely weaned when it no longer requires any hand-feeding to maintain its weight. Chicks should be monitored closely for a minimum of 7-10 days after the last day of hand-feeding. At this point, if they are eating and cracking seed as well as eating the soft foods offered, they will usually gain a little weight and level off.

The chick must be eating enough to maintain its weight to be considered weaned. If small weight losses are noticed it may be helpful to offer small quantities of hand-feeding formula once a day to help stimulate their appetite. Never fill the crop to capacity during weaning as this will often cause vomiting and regression to a formula dependent chick. If weight loss is excessive, offer small amounts of formula several times a day in addition to weaning foods.

11.5 Caging During Weaning

Because birds are also stretching their wings and preparing for their first flight at about the same time as they are weaning, they will need to be caged or wing-clipped so they will remain where you want them. Chicks should be provided with a perch, mounted low in the cage, so they can learn to perch in a natural manner. Food bowls should be placed on the bottom of the cage, at first, so the birds will not have to try to keep their balance as well as learn to eat.

Weaning cages can be constructed of virtually any caging wire. Build a simple cube-type cage that is large enough that the bird can turn around without damaging its tail feathers. It is not wise to put chicks in cages when they still have numerous blood feathers in the wings or tail as these may break and begin to bleed. Also be cautious about the wire used on the bottom of the cage since the birds' toes can get caught in this. It is not recommended to layer wire bottoms because this creates a gap between the two pieces that will catch a toe or foot. When a regular bird cage is used for weaning, a layer of 1/2 inch by 1/2 inch wire may have to be placed on top of the bottom grates. Inspect the way the wire fits to see if there is room for impending danger. Young chicks do not understand when a foot is restrained and may pull until they break a leg or toe. Check cages for safety hazards before placing chicks inside. Keep all weaning cages clean of feces and food debris to reduce the possibility of bacterial and fungal growth.

Sun Conures in a weaning cage.

11.6 Potential Problems During Weaning

During the weaning process many things can go wrong. A common occurrence would be where a young chick swallows an entire crop full of whole uncracked seed. The digestive tract is usually not capable of digesting this and crop impacting occurs. Veterinary assistance is necessary to remove the seed from the crop. Whole grapes or very large chunks of vegetables will usually cause this problem also, and may have to be removed before digestion is hampered. Consult sections **10.2** and **10.3** on removing foreign objects from the crop.

Another common situation is when a young bird catches its blood feathers on the weaning cage and begins to bleed. Always keep some type of coagulating agent on hand when young chicks are present in the nursery.

Many young birds have been lost forever by flying out of their weaning cage and through an open window or door. The shame of it all is that these birds do not know how to eat and will eventually starve to death. Setting traps for these birds is usually futile as they are new at flying and will usually fly up, not down. Clipping a wing or checking the room for potential escape routes will help to eliminate the problem.

11.7 Weight Losses During Weaning

During the conversion from being hand-fed to eating seeds and other foods, birds do experience a certain amount of normal weight loss. Hand-fed babies that are fed properly and receive the correct nutrition will usually top normal adult weights for their species prior to weaning. During the weaning process weight losses should be monitored daily to assure the chick does not get too thin. Once weaned, the bird's weight will often rise again to its maintainable adult weight.

If baby birds are fat and healthy when they begin to wean, it is safe to allow weight loss up to about 15-18% of their beginning body weight. Anytime a chick looks or feels thin or has reached its maximum weight loss, hand-feeding should be increased in an attempt to restore lost body weight. This is not to say that they should be fed four times a day, but perhaps a small amount in the morning and a full crop just prior to sleeping at night. As they learn to eat from the food bowl, once again hand-feeding can be reduced. Continue this on-again off-again feeding until the bird is maintaining its weight by itself. Foods of high fat content such as nuts or seeds will be of benefit to chicks that are losing too much weight. If they insist on filling their crops on apples, carrots or other low fat foods, these may have to be offered in limited quantities in order to force the chick to eat seeds.

11.8 Imprinting (Positive and Negatives)

The imprinting (humanization) that takes place in hand-fed parrots can work for the good or the detriment of your avicultural goals. Chicks that are being reared for the pet trade need to be gentle, humanized specimens. Those that are being raised for future breeding programs, due to their rarity or economic value, should be raised in a way that they will not be imprinted on humans or where its effects will be minimal.

Certain species of parrots, once imprinted, will rarely be of any value as breeding stock. They can grow up to view a potential mate as their competition for human affection. This can become a dangerous situation when dealing with Cockatoos as the imprinted male may kill his female mate. Socialization with their own kind and observation of adult courtship behavior may in some cases change a bird's attitude, but usually behavioral change takes a long time to evolve.

The ease at which some parrots do imprint on humans makes these species ideal pet companions. Many times an added plus is the mimicry or talking ability that accompanies the imprinting. The friendliest, chattiest, most humanized birds are the ones sought after as pets in the pet shop. Through hand-rearing and constant human interaction it is possible to raise the ideal pet bird.

It is important that each bird be raised in the manner appropriate for its future use. Research the species that you are keeping so imprinting can be controlled if needed to reduce the unnecessary stress in the bird's life. Chicks that are destined to become pet companion birds can be handled frequently to eliminate their fear of humans. Any birds being raised to be used as breeding stock will be better breeders if raised in a less humanized surrounding. Future breeders can be brooded in brown paper bags to assimilate the dark nest boxes they will be given in the future. They should only be handled during feeding and physical inspection and once weaned they should be caged with birds of their own species or genus so they can begin the socialization process.

There are exceptions to all these rules. Many times an imprinted bird will grow up to make an excellent breeder. This seems to be more prevalent in the smaller species of Conures and in some Asian parrots that have a greater tendency to revert to wild behavior after weaning. Cockatoos, Amazons, and some Macaws, however, may never produce fertile eggs if they are imprinted on humans and are never given the opportunity to socialize with their own kind. Hand-reared breeders are less afraid of humans and if raised in the manner described above, and socialized with their own kind at a young age, will often turn out to be calm, excellent aviary breeders.

11.9   Weaning-Psychology of the Young

Although imprinting is an important step in creating the ideal companion bird, the relationship that is built between bird and owner during, and directly after, the weaning process will be what dictates the type of long-term relationship the owner has with his bird. The ideal situation would be to have the bird look upon you as a respected and affectionate parent rather than a sibling or a member of the flock.

The most important method of achieving this goal is to establish yourself, and anyone else who wishes to have the same status with the bird, as a primary source of physical affection. As the bird grows older, cuddling and holding lose their value and preening rises in importance as the major form of how physical affection is shared. Parent birds spend large amounts of time preening their young and this becomes more important to the older chick than the act of feeding. As in all children they will test you to see just how much they can get away with and just how hard they can nip you. When this is done you must define the relationship by not allowing them to get away with a wrongdoing as a sibling or flock member would.

With some birds, like African Greys, a harsh verbal retort and a puff of air blown at the bird's head is usually enough to let them know you are not happy with their behavior. In other more physical species, such as Macaws or Amazons, grabbing the upper mandible firmly between thumb and forefinger and slightly shaking the head may be necessary if the puff of air is ignored. If this fails to put the bird in its place, and many times it will with Scarlet Macaws and Yellow-Naped Amazons, a light tap on the upper mandible with your forefinger might be in order. Although this may be necessary it should only be done to species that do it to each other during natural interaction. Amazons and Macaws do this to one another for the same reason that you would do it to them. African Greys, on the other hand, do not physically reprimand each other in that way and a light cuff on the beak of a pet African Grey might ruin the relationship for life. An Amazon or Macaw will usually forget the punishment within five minutes.

This type of behavior correction should only be used after you have established yourself as a primary source of physical affection to the bird. Many times the initial reaction will be a startled look. It can be advantageous at this point to follow up your move of aggression by a slow reach to the back of the bird's head to begin the act of preening. This helps to establish your image as the stern but affectionate parent. Although many pet owners accept the rough and tumble play with mock biting as acceptable interaction, this type of interaction should be discouraged as it undermines your standing as a respected parent image and places you more into the category of a sibling companion. This will also allow the bird to believe that it can eventually place you somewhere below it in the pecking order.

During and directly after the weaning stage is the most

important time to develop and solidify your relationship with the bird. If ignored at this crucial time, the bird may not respond to affection and will not become the tame companion-bird that you desire. If you don't spend a lot of time with your bird at this point you may lose many of the hand-raised qualities that you are looking for. If you maximize the time that you spend with the bird in these few months, ignoring him for six months out of the year somewhere down the line, will have minimal effect on its tameness.

11.10 Caution: Weaning Regression

In some cases when hand-feeding is discontinued, babies will panic and revert to extreme dependency. This can occur even if the chick has been eating on its own and maintaining its weight for quite some time. Parrots, being very oral animals, have to make the psychological connection between eating and the satisfaction of hunger.

The tongue is used to inspect and play with new things that gain their interest. This playing often leads to swallowing if the object in the mouth is of a manageable size and is the reason why so many babies tend to swallow bedding material or substrate. The chicks are attracted to the weaning food as something to play with, not something to eat. The eventual swallowing of the food is a natural progression of their desire to touch things with their tongues and to put them into their mouths. When hand-feeding is discontinued they will often panic when they realize that food is no longer being delivered directly into their beaks and will often stop playing with their food and begin to get very hungry. Chicks that have reverted completely may sit around all the time and cry to be fed even if the crop is full. These birds are usually very difficult to wean and may take as long as six months before they begin once again to eat on their own. The quantity of formula that is hand-fed each day should be limited to try to force the chick to eat the weaning food. Once the chick is eating and maintaining a good weight and refuses the hand-feeding for about seven to ten days, the feeding of formula can be discontinued.

11.11 Who is Responsible for Weaning the Chicks?

Those who are not familiar with the parrot personality will wonder why baby parrots are often not weaned on the farm where they are produced, but in a pet shop or in the home of the eventual owner. There are many reasons for this and most are related to the effect that weaning will have on the personality of the bird. Shipping birds that are still hand-feeding has a less stressful effect on them. In the wild, the chicks would be sitting in a dark nesting cavity quite similar to the environment provided by an airline shipping crate. A baby parrot that has not yet weaned feels perfectly secure in this type of dark environment, unlike those that have weaned and fledged and are used to their freedom of movement.

It is a fact that newly weaned chicks may become stressed easier and react much worse than older birds that are shipped. Perhaps adult birds are better able to handle the psycological effect of shipping than newly weaned chicks. If they are still being hand-fed, then shipping seems like being moved to another brooder.

The pet shop has a major influence on the socialization process of a chick. This is due to the tremendous variety of people that the chick will come in contact with. If weaned chicks are sent from the breeder and are not used to many people being around

Elisha and Stacie Voren display a basket of Amazons ready for market.

them they may react with fear or apprehension. Hand-feeding babies will adjust to the new environment in a day or two whereas weaned babies may completely forget about eating on their own and will not allow anyone unfamiliar to feed them. The chick that is still being hand-fed will usually accept any set of hands to feed it.

Another good reason for weaning chicks in the pet store is that they will become better companion birds if they are fed in the presence of the eventual owner. Even if they are not fed by, or in the presence of, the new owner, they will be better socialized in the pet store during the very impressionable weaning stage. This type of socialization is not possible, or very limited, on the breeding farm. It is still a fact that a minimum of stress will occur if the chick is shipped before weaning and at the same time the baby will grow up to be the type of companion that the eventual owner will want.